THE BIBLE

AND

MODERN SCIENCE

HENRY M. MORRIS, Ph.D.

MOODY PRESS ● CHICAGO

CONTENTS

THE BIBLE AND MODERN SCIENCE

A MOODY PRESS BOOK
Copyright © 1951, 1968
by The Moody Bible Institute of Chicago
All rights reserved
Printed in the United States of America

PREFACE

THE PURPOSE of this book, very frankly and without apology, is to win people to a genuine faith in Jesus Christ as the eternal Son of God and the Bible as the Word of God, and to help strengthen the faith of those who already believe. The Christian faith is not founded on wishful thinking or blind acceptance of tradition, but rather on a tremendous body of real, objective evidence.

It is the aim of this little book to present in summary form some of this evidence, as well as to answer the most frequently raised objections to biblical Christianity. The evidences and questions discussed are mostly of an objective type, rather than subjective or philosophic. The reader should realize, of course, that the evidence can never be presented with sufficient force to compel its acceptance in a mind which is already closed to the possibility of its truth. Otherwise, there would be no room for a free moral choice, and God desires that we come to Him willingly, in faith and love and gratitude.

Nevertheless, there is so much evidence available as basis for faith in Christ and His Word that one may find more than ample "reason for the hope," if he examines it with an open mind and willing heart. Having studied most of the basic sciences, having belonged to many scientific societies and associated with scientists and intellectuals daily for thirty years, having taught in five great universities for twenty-six years, having read thousands of books and articles on various scientific subjects—and at the same time having averaged over one hour every day for over twenty-seven years in the study of the Bible—he is firmly convinced that every word of the Bible is inspired of God, absolutely free of error, with innumerable marks of divine inspiration throughout its pages. But, and perhaps more significantly, this objective conviction has been abundantly confirmed through the years by the experimental reality of the living Christ, dwelling in the heart by faith, supplying every need and making full provision for all "peace and joy in believing."

The Lord has already graciously used this book in its earlier editions. First issued in 1946, under the title *That You Might Believe,* it was later expanded and first published under its present title in 1951. A paperback condensation was then prepared and issued in 1957. Over 150,000 copies have been printed. Editions have been published in Spanish and Braille and, in part, in Chinese and Portuguese. The continued demand seems to warrant an updating of the book at this time.

In the previous edition, it was noted that the writer's wife and six children united with him in prayer that our gracious God and Father would bless and use the book. This prayer has been abundantly answered, as we have met and learned of many who have been helped to a saving faith in Christ and to a fruitful ministry in His service in part because of it. Our prayer now is thus both one of thanksgiving for those who have read it in years past and one of continued intercession for those who will do so in years to come.

HENRY M. MORRIS

1

MODERN SCIENCE IN THE BIBLE

ONE OF THE MOST arresting evidences of the inspiration of the Bible is the great number of scientific truths that have lain hidden within its pages for thirty centuries or more, only to be discovered by man's enterprise within the last few centuries or even years. Let us look at a few of these.

Consider the field of astronomy. For thousands of years, many wise men have busied themselves with counting the stars and constellations. Before the invention of the telescope in the seventeenth century, the number of the stars was regarded as practically determined. The great Ptolemy gave the number as 1,056. Tycho Brahe cataloged 777 and Kepler counted 1,005. This number has since been tremendously increased, of course, and the end is not yet even remotely in view. It is now known that there are well over 100 billions of stars in our own galaxy, with probably billions of other galaxies like our own. Most astronomers now agree that it is not humanly possible to count all the stars. This would not have been admitted by scientists a few centuries ago. But the Bible makes the assertion over and over again. One such instance is in Jeremiah 33:22, "The host of heaven *cannot* be numbered."

As another example, look at Job 26:7, "He . . . hangeth the earth upon nothing." That sounds amazingly like twentieth century science! Even the existence of the hypothetical space substance called ether is now believed by most physicists and astronomers to have been disproved. The attraction of gravity is invoked to account for the earth's affinity to the sun, but that explains nothing. No one knows what gravity is or why it is. It is merely a term invented to explain certain observed phenomena. Truly, there is nothing that modern science can add to or take away from the age-old statement that God has hung the earth upon nothing.

Or consider Isaiah 40:22, where speaking of God, the prophet says: "It is he who sitteth upon the circle of the earth." The word translated "circle" is the Hebrew *khug,* a more exact connotation of which is "sphericity" or "roundness."

Psalm 19 was long a source of amusement to Bible critics. In speaking of the sun, the psalmist says: "His going forth is from the end of the heaven, and his circuit unto the ends of it: and there is nothing hid from the heat thereof." It was claimed that the writer of this verse obviously believed in the ancient notion of the sun's revolving about the earth.

This charge is most unjust, since we still use words and phrases of the same sort, simply because from our natural viewpoint the sun does rise in the morning, move across the sky, and set in the evening. The whole science of nautical and engineering astronomy is based on the assumption, made purely for convenience, that the earth is the center of a great celestial sphere, moving along the surface of which in ordered paths are the sun, moon, planets and stars. And as far as any practical usage is concerned, this is so. On this assumption, courses can be plotted, positions determined, and scores of other applications made.

But the words of the psalmist may have a deeper, more truly scientific meaning than that. It is now believed by the leading astronomers that the sun, with the entire solar system, actually does move through space at the tremendous speed of 600,000 miles per hour in such a gigantic orbit that it requires over two million centuries to complete it. Furthermore, it is probable that our galaxy is also moving with respect to other galaxies. The sun's circuit *is* from one end of the heavens to the other! Who can accuse the Holy Spirit of ignorance of modern astronomy?

It is glorious to realize that the great Astronomer and Mathematician who created the heavens, setting all the stars and universes of stars in their appointed courses, and who, according to Psalm 147, ". . . calleth them all by their names," is the same One who calls you and me to eternal life in Jesus Christ!

But let us look into the science of meteorology for a moment. The "water cycle," whereby water is precipitated as rain or snow, then drained off by the river system into the ocean, whence it is raised by evaporation back into the skies and carried by the wind back to the land to be again precipitated, is a fundamental fact of this comparatively new field of science. Yet this fact was strikingly set forth in the Bible ages before men discovered it. Furthermore, it is now well known that the major wind currents of the world follow well-defined circuits. These great wind circuits are largely responsible for all the great ocean currents as well as the great air currents of the world. But this great truth is a matter of comparatively recent discovery. Now read Ecclesiastes 1:6-7, set down by King Solomon three thousand years ago: "The wind goeth toward the south, and turneth about unto the north; it whirleth about continually, and the wind returneth again according to his circuits. All the rivers run into the sea; yet the sea is not full; unto the place from whence the rivers come, thither they return again." No wonder we speak of the wisdom of Solomon! But isn't it pertinent to ask how he happened to know these things when no one else knew them until thousands of years later?

Also consider the words of Elihu in Job 36:27-29

(ASV, margin): "For he draweth up the drops of water, which distill in rain from the vapor thereof, which the skies pour down and drop upon man abundantly. Yea, can any understand the spreadings of the clouds, the thunderings of his pavilion?" This passage is a most excellent, concise summary of those phases of the hydrologic cycle involving the very marvelous physical processes of evaporation, condensation, and precipitation.

There is very much for science yet to learn concerning the details of the processes of the water cycle. Each phase of the cycle is absolutely necessary for life to exist on the earth, and offers abundant testimony to its origin at the hands of an infinitely wise, beneficent Creator. There are many more references in Scripture to various phases of the sciences of hydrology and meteorology, all remarkably in accord with the most up-to-date studies in these fields.

It is very significant that the medical and sanitary laws and regulations of Moses were very far in advance of the times. To see this, one need only compare the customs and beliefs of the ancient Egyptians and Babylonians, for instance, with those of the Hebrews as given to them in the books of Moses. For example, in Leviticus 11 is found a list of animals, fishes, birds, and insects that the Israelites could regard as clean and fit to eat. The criterion of both chewing the cud and parting the hoof was set as a guide to the clean animals. We still go by the same rule, except that we eat also the pig, the rabbit, and the hare, which were prohibited to the Jews by this rule. It is now known, however, that these latter animals are easily subject to parasitic infection and are safe only if they have been cleanly fed and have been well cooked before eating. The birds and fish the Israelites were permitted to eat are the same as those now known to modern medical knowledge to be the safest and best. The only insects allowed for food were certain locusts, beetles and grasshoppers, which are now known to be clean feeders, and safe for human consumption. They are still eaten in large quantities in other parts of the world and are evidently quite satisfactory as food.

In Deuteronomy 14:21, Moses forbade the Jews to eat the flesh of any animal that had died a natural death, in spite of the fact that they lived in desert regions and their flocks were very essential sources of food. This is still regarded as such good advice that similar laws are in force in most civilized countries today.

The subjects of water supply and sewage disposal are of great interest and import to both bacteriologists and civil engineers, as well as to the general public. It was not until the last century that the significance of a clean and sanitary water supply in the prevention of disease was recognized. But Moses seemed to understand something of modern bacteriology, because he forbade the drinking of water from small or stagnant pools, or from water that had been contaminated by coming in contact with animals or meat. (See Lev. 11:29-36.) In Deuteronomy 23:12-14, directions were given for the disposal of sanitary sewage by burial. All of these sanitary regulations, as well as those concerning the personal cleanliness of the body, were far in advance of the practices in even the so-called civilized countries of the world until within the past hundred years. This is true also of the prescribed segregation and treatment of such diseases as leprosy.

Not only were the scientific and medical laws of Moses far ahead of the times, but so were the civil laws. It is well known that the laws of Moses form the basis of the law systems of all the great democratic nations of the world today. Although it is true that the early Babylonians and Hittites had codes of laws that were similar in some respects to those of Moses, it is also true that they were not nearly as logical, just or complete, as those in the Pentateuch. Even more important, the Hebrew law was unique in that it centered everything else in the worship and serving of one God, Jehovah, a concept utterly foreign to the Babylonians and Hittites of that day.

The great truth revealed in Leviticus 17:11 and a number of other Scriptures concerning the preeminent importance of the blood in the biological mechanism, has only been comprehended with any adequacy in recent years: "For the life of the flesh is in the blood. . . ."

Continuance of life depends upon the continued supply of oxygen, water and food to the cells of all parts of the body. This absolutely necessary function is accomplished in a marvelous manner by the blood as it circulates constantly throughout the body, year after year. The function of blood in combating disease-producing organisms and in repairing injured tissues is one of the most significant discoveries of modern medical science, and the use of blood transfusions as one of the most beneficial treatments for nearly every kind of disease further testifies to the supremacy of the blood in the life of the flesh.

The Word of God was scientifically accurate in this great biological truth thousands of years before man discovered and elaborated it. Yet it was given primarily to teach an even greater spiritual truth—the necessity of the shedding of blood in sacrifice for the remission of sins. The blood, which is the channel of life, becomes also the carrier of disease and infection through the body when they gain the upper hand in the system. Physical life symbolizes spiritual life, and physical death symbolizes spiritual death. Physical disease and injury symbolize the spiritual disease of sin.

As the infection of sin spreads throughout the soul, it will ultimately produce eternal spiritual death. If spiritual life is to be produced and maintained, new life must be introduced from without, life untainted with sin and containing the power to combat the ravages of sin in the spiritually dying soul. In figure, a transfusion of blood is essential, and it must be from a qualified donor whose blood possesses the purity and efficacy required for the salvation of the spiritually dying soul.

This is the merest glimpse of the depths of spiritual (and even biological) meaning in the biblical doctrine of substitutionary sacrifice. "Without shedding of blood is no forgiveness" (Heb. 9:22, margin). This was the symbolism of the animal sacrifices of the Mosaic law. It finds its ultimate and universal culmination in the sacrificial death of the Son of God for the sins of the world. Jesus said: "This is my blood of the covenant, which is poured out for many for the forgiveness of sins" (Matt. 26:28, RSV).

By virtue of Jesus' atoning death, each one who receives by faith His life—poured out unto death, but raised up again by the power of God—receives forgiveness and cleansing of all sin, and in fact receives Christ Himself. All this is symbolized by the shed blood. Jesus said: "Whoso eateth my flesh, and drinketh my blood, hath eternal life; and I will raise him up at the last day. . . . He that eateth my flesh, and drinketh my blood, dwelleth in me, and I in him" (John 6:54, 56).

Many other examples of scientific truth in Scripture could be cited from practically every field of physical, biological or social science. One further example, which is very important, will be given.

The basic principal of all physical science is that of the conservation and deterioration of energy. The law of energy conservation states that in any transformation of energy in a closed system from one sort into another, the total amount of energy remains unchanged.

A similar law is the law of mass conservation, which states that although matter may be changed in size, state, form, etc., the total mass cannot be changed. In other words, these laws teach that no creation or destruction of matter or energy is now being accomplished anywhere in the physical universe.

This law is absolutely basic and of prime importance in all physical science (the law of mass conservation is actually a special part of the law of energy conservation). It was demonstrated quantitatively by science only about a hundred years ago. However, the Bible has taught for thousands of years the same great truth that creation is no longer going on (contrary to the philosophy of continual evolutionary creation), but rather that the present system is merely the result of an original divine creation, which of course is something that would not be susceptible of experimental study at the present time. For example, Hebrews 4:3 affirms: "The works were finished from the foundation of the world." Genesis 2:1-2 says: "Thus the heavens and the earth were finished, and all the host of them. And on the seventh day God ended his work which he had made."

This law of mass and energy conservation is also known as the first law of thermodynamics, and is almost without controversy the most important and basic law of all physical science. As we have just seen, it was anticipated by the biblical record of a finished creation.

The second law of thermodynamics, of almost as great significance, enunciates the corollary law of energy deterioration. In any energy transfer or change, although the total amount of energy remains unchanged, the amount of usefulness and availability that the energy possesses is always decreased. This principle is also called the law of entropy increase, "entropy" being a sort of mathematical abstraction which is actually a measure of the nonavailability of the energy of a system.

Thus, in any closed mechanical system, regardless how large or how small, the energy of the system must continually be degraded, as long as any energy change is taking place in the system—with some of the energy being dissipated in nonrecoverable friction or heat energy. Since all activities of nature (including biological activities) involve such energy transfers, there must be an ever decreasing supply of usable energy for maintaining such processes in the universe as a whole.

This law of entropy increase is responsible for the fact that no machine can be constructed to 100 percent efficiency and that a perpetual motion machine is impossible. It is of primary importance in the writer's fields of fluid mechanics and hydrology, and in all other disciplines of physical science as well.

Practically all the earth's energy, except its atomic energy, comes, or has come, from the sun. However, by far the greater part of the tremendous amount of energy that the sun is continually radiating is dissipated in space in the form of unrecoverable heat energy. This prodigious waste of energy cannot last forever. Eventually, barring supernatural intervention, the sun must burn itself out, and then all activity on the earth must cease as well. The same principle applies to all the stars of the universe, so that the physical universe is, beyond question, growing old, wearing out and running down.

But this law certainly testifies equally to the necessary truth that the universe had a definite beginning. If it is growing old, it must once have been young; if it is wearing out, it must once have been new; if it is running down, it must first have been "wound up." In short, this law of energy degeneration conveys us back inexorably to an affirmation of the necessary truth of the existence of a Creator, and a definite creation, which must have taken place in the past but which, according to the law of mass and energy conservation, is *not* continuing in the present.

But now let us note the teaching of Scripture concerning this principle of deterioration. For example, Psalm 102:25-27 says: "Of old hast thou laid the foundation of the earth: and the heavens are the work of thy hands. They shall perish, but thou shalt endure: yea, *all of them shall wax old like a garment;* as a vesture shalt thou change them, and they shall be changed. But thou art the same, and thy years shall have no end."

There are many other passages of similar import in the Bible. Thus, the Scripture teaches that which science has only discovered in the past hundred years, namely, that in spite of an original completed creation, the universe is aging and heading inexorably toward ultimate physical death.

However, the Bible also speaks often of that which science cannot discover: a future supernatural intervention of the Creator in His creation, destruction of the present system, and creation of "new heavens and a new earth," which "shall continue" and "wherein dwelleth righteousness" (Rev. 21:1; Isa. 65:17; 66:22; II Peter 3:13).

An allied truth to these just considered, alluded to previously, is also indicated in Scripture. This is the basic equivalence of mass and energy, one of the most important discoveries of twentieth century science. It is well known now that matter is actually one form of energy, or better, is a manifestation of that form of energy known as atomic energy. The source of the tremendous energy of the atom is yet unknown and may be, in fact, undiscoverable by science. However, it is certain that a tremendous supply of energy from some source (or rather, tremendous power, since power is the *rate* of energy supply or expenditure) is necessary to maintain the terrific motions and forces associated with the various subatomic particles. The magnitudes of such energies are graphically intimated in the energy released by atomic disintegration.

Most significant, then, is the proclamation of Hebrews 1:2-3: "God . . . hath in these last days spoken unto us by his Son, whom he hath appointed heir of all things, by whom also he made the worlds; who being the brightness of his glory, and the express image of his person, and *upholding all things by the world of his power,* when he had by himself purged our sins, sat down on the right hand of the Majesty on high."

This passage teaches that all *things*—that is, the matter of the physical universe—are maintained by energy or *power,* the source of which is the Creator Himself, the Lord Jesus Christ!

The same tremendous truth is taught in Colossians 1:17, which is accurately translated in the American Standard Version: ". . . in him [Christ] all things *hold together*" (margin).

Then in Hebrews 11:3 appears the following remarkably scientific statement: "Through faith we understand that the worlds were framed by the word of God, so that *things which are seen* were *not* made of *things which do appear.*" In other words, the matter of the universe is not ultimately physical but is composed of something which is *not "apparent."*

The Greek word for "worlds" in this verse means "world-times" and, in this context, might well refer to the nature of the universe as a *continuum* of space, mass and time, thus anticipating the modern scientific and relativistic view of the universe. Not only does this statement again emphasize the fact that the material substance of the universe is upheld by the divine Word, but even more that it came into existence by that Word. That is, the universe was not produced out of preexisting chaotic matter of some kind; rather, it was created *ex nihilo*—"out of nothing"—nothing apparent to the physical senses, that is, but out of the infinite reservoir of energy of the all-powerful Word of God. It is significant that this marvelous "faith" chapter, Hebrews 11, begins with such an eloquent assertion of the necessity of understanding by faith the fact of a primeval special creation.

We have now looked at approximately a score of examples of modern scientific knowledge recorded in Scripture thousands of years before they were discovered by man. This ought to be abundantly convincing evidence of the supernatural source and inspiration of the Bible. But now let us examine briefly some of the best known examples of supposed scientific error or contradiction in the Bible.

The ancient question, "Where did Cain get his wife?" has always been the stock objection of shallow-thinking critics. The story of Cain, who was probably, although it is not definitely so stated, the eldest son of Adam and Eve, is found in Genesis 4. It is stated that, as a result of his murder of Abel, he was condemned by God to be "a fugitive and a vagabond." He went out to the land of Nod, on the east of Eden, where according to verse 17, "Cain knew his wife; and she conceived, and bare Enoch: and he builded a city." This is gleefully pointed to as a glaring inconsistency, since Cain is supposed to have been the only person living at that time, other than Adam and Eve.

However, this supposition is entirely unwarranted. Nowhere is the statement made that he was the only living child of Adam at that time. It is stated elsewhere, however, that Adam had sons and daughters, mentioning, in addition, that he lived 800 years after the birth of Seth, who was probably, though not necessarily, his third child. In all, Adam lived 930 years. The general rule of that day seemed to be longevity and prolificness. In fact, the first command given Adam and Eve was to "be fruitful and multiply." Furthermore, the ability to have children seemed not to be much reduced by advancing age. It is stated that Noah, for example, was 500 years old before he begat Shem, Ham and Japheth.

These years, incidentally, are not to be understood as shorter than our years, as there is no substantial basis for this belief. Although we may not be able actually to prove or disprove the longevity of the ancients, at least the Bible is consistent within itself.

If we accept then the implication that men lived hundreds of years and continued to have sons and daughters most of their lives, and then adopt marriage and birth rates that are very conservative compared with our present rates, it can be calculated quickly that there were at least twenty million people on the earth at the time of Adam's death. There would have been an ample selection from which Cain could choose a wife in plenty of time to build a great many cities. Of course, *some* son of Adam had to marry his sister. But it is foolish to assert that, in that early day before disease and the evils of inbred heredity had begun to have the effects they have now, such a union would result in feebleminded or deformed offspring.

Other questions, such as evolution and great length of life, that would affect the above discussion are considered in more detail later. In any event, it should now be clear that the Bible is not inconsistent within itself on the matter of Cain's wife.

The story of Jonah and the whale also has been difficult for many to believe. It was formerly claimed that no whale possessed a gullet large enough to admit a man, for example. However, it is now known that there is at least one whale, the sperm whale, which inhabits the Mediterranean, which is quite capable of swallowing a much larger object than a man. There are also a number of other fish with sufficiently large gullets, and it may be significant that the Bible account speaks only of a "great fish," not necessarily a whale. There have even been a number of accounts, some of them well authenticated, of men in modern times having been swallowed by the sperm whale or some other sea monster, and then later being rescued alive. However, if necessary, there is no reason for us to refuse to believe in an actual miraculous intervention by God in the preservation of Jonah's life. It is even possible that Jonah actually died and was then restored to life by God, as Lazarus and others recorded in Scripture. The Lord Jesus (Matt. 12:40) accepted the story of Jonah as authentic history, and even used it as a type or symbol of His own coming death and resurrection.

We shall consider one other case in this chapter— the long day of Joshua. This supposedly incredible story is found in Joshua 10. In the great battle between the Israelites and the confederation of the Amorites, it is related how "the Lord fought for Israel" by two miracles: (1) causing the sun and moon to "be inactive" (not "stand still" as incorrectly rendered in the translation) and "hasting not to go down about the space of a whole day" in order to give the children of Israel time to completely defeat the Amorites before nightfall; (2) sending a great hailstorm, which probably served the twofold purpose of giving Joshua's army relief from the terrific heat and of slaying large numbers of the enemy. One frequent objection to this story is that it speaks of the sun stopping its revolution about the earth, whereas it is really not the sun but the earth which is moving. However, elementary physics recognizes that any motion must be measured in relation to some *assumed* fixed point of reference. The location of this point (since a point of absolute fixity in the universe is completely unknown) is totally arbitrary and should be chosen in the way that best meets the convenience of the observer. The selection of the earth's surface as the reference plane by which to measure the motion of the sun and moon, as Joshua did, is thus perfectly logical and scientific.

Another objection is that, if the earth suddenly stopped rotating on its axis, everything on the surface would be violently dislocated and probably destroyed. However, there is no intimation that the stoppage was sudden instead of gradual. (If an automobile traveling at high speed is instantaneously stopped, great damage ensues to its occupants; but if it gradually slows to a halt, they of course feel no disturbance.) It is true, however, that the circulation of the atmosphere would be affected, since it is controlled to some extent by the earth's rotation. This fact probably accounts for the tremendous hailstorm which accompanied the miracle.

If this event actually took place, accomplished by a temporary slowing down of the rotational speed of the earth, it would be reasonable to suppose that people over the whole earth would have noticed it and made some record of it. However, these would now be preserved, if at all, only in the form of semimythical recollections of the event handed down in the folklore of these peoples, since written records of that period (about 1400 B.C.) have not been found at all, except in the Bible and in the fragmentary records of certain nations near the eastern shore of the Mediterranean.

It is significant, therefore, that intimations of such an event can be noted in the mythologies of many peoples from various parts of the earth. So frequent is the occurrence of these, in fact, that they have even been used to bolster the theory that the biblical account was derived from them. For example, T. W. Doane in his book *Bible Myths*[1] describes accounts of a long day, similar to that of the Bible, in the Orphic hymns, in the legends of the Hindus, the Buddhists, the Chinese, the ancient Mexicans and others, and then

[1] T. W. Doane, *Bible Myths* (New York: Truth Seeker, 1882) p. 91.

draws the very dubious conclusion that the biblical record was therefore derived from such as these.

One of the most persistent of the legends of the various American Indian tribes is that of the theft of the sun for a day, according to M. W. Stirling, in the 1945 Report of the Smithsonian Institute, as well as numerous other ethnologists. A very similar legend is found among the Polynesians. The Greek legend of Phaethon, who disrupted the sun's course for a day, could easily have been derived from this event. Herodotus, the Greek historian, states that the priests of Egypt showed him records of such a day. Other mythological reflections of the long day might also be noted, but it should already be evident that the account in the book of Joshua is accompanied by semimythical records from all parts of the world, of just the sort that one would expect to find if the event had actually taken place.

The long day was undoubtedly a supernatural event, but in view of the fact of the existence of a personal God, interested in His creation and its ultimate purpose, it is foolish to say, as some have said, that miracles are impossible. God has planned and maintained a very efficiently working universe, normally subject to the operation of its regular laws. However, it is eminently reasonable that, if God's purposes were better served thereby, He would be expected on occasions to intervene in the normal operation of the so-called "natural laws." In fact, even these laws, as we have seen, along with all things in the physical universe, are actually upheld and maintained directly by the power of God.

The question then in the case of any alleged miracle is not whether it *could* happen, but whether it *did* happen. The question should certainly be decided in the affirmative if both of the following conditions are satisfied: (1) that there existed adequate reason, in line with God's ultimate purposes, for God to intervene in the normally operative laws of nature; (2) that there exists adequate testimonial or other evidence to its actual occurrence, evidence such as would be judged adequate to prove other factual matters, not necessarily miraculous in nature.

It is believed that both these conditions are abundantly satisfied in all of the biblical miracles. With regard to Joshua's long day, there was quite sufficient reason for God to perform such a miracle at this time. The success of Joshua's entire campaign depended on victory in this battle, and thus also the fulfillment of God's promises to the world through the nation Israel. Furthermore, the Canaanite peoples were sun worshipers, and it may well have been that God chose to accomplish their defeat through the instrumentality of their supposed god, in order to demonstrate better the falsity of their exceedingly cruel and licentious religious system. It should also be remembered that the miracle followed immediately upon Joshua's command, uttered no doubt as a prayer of implicit faith. God answers prayer many times in very remarkable ways, as all who truly know the Lord Jesus can testify. He has even promised to remove mountains in answer to genuine faith. He had made a specific promise to Joshua in regard to the Canaanite campaign and this particular battle. If needed, still other reasons might be adduced to indicate the necessity for this miracle.

As to the evidence for it, the very fact that the story appears in the Bible is itself strong evidence. As we shall see later, the historical portions of the Bible have been substantiated in scores of instances by archaeological research, including especially many phases of Joshua's conquests. Historically, the Bible is now believed by nearly all authorities in Palestinian archaeology, even by those who deny its supernatural inspiration, to be a very valuable and trustworthy book. Also, as we shall see, there are many other independent lines of evidence corroborative of the doctrine of inspiration.

Joshua (or perhaps a later copyist) was able also to appeal in his account to a corroborative account of the miracle in the then-extant book of Jasher. Finally, we have already noted the existence of many semilegendary recollections of such an event throughout the various areas of the world. These alone are sufficient to establish the strong probability of the historicity of the biblical account.

The widely publicized theories of Velikovsky may be mentioned in this connection, according to which the earth has experienced a number of severe physical catastrophes in the past. These were attributed by him to the near approaches of a huge comet to the earth, one of which he supposed caused the stopping of the earth's rotation in the days of Joshua. Dr. Velikovsky amassed a really impressive amount of evidence from the myths and legends of many peoples that such a "long day" had actually been recorded and observed all over the world. However, his explanation of its cause is beset by many difficulties and has not been taken seriously by scientists; his whole work therefore is largely ignored. Nevertheless, he did point out a great amount of evidence supporting the *fact* of the long day, even though his ideas concerning its *cause* were unscientific (and, of course, unscriptural as well).

We shall close this chapter with a very brief and inadequate mention of the most sacred and most profound doctrine of the Holy Scriptures—the doctrine of the triune God. All true Christians believe in God the Father, God the Son, and God the Holy Spirit, and that these three, though distinct from one point of view, constitute only one God. Many, of course, have scoffed at this belief that God is one Person and, at the same time, three Persons. It is contrary to established and inalterable mathematical principles, they say, for Christians to maintain that $1 + 1 + 1 = 1$, rather than 3. It is unscientific and foolish, they are agreed, that the God of the universe (even though they should grant for the moment that He might be a real personality) could be both one personality and three personalities at the same time. Therefore, it follows for them, that Jesus was not God in the biblical sense at all.

However, as Dr. Nathan Wood, former president of Gordon College, has shown in a very remarkable volume, the doctrine of the Trinity is not only sound mathematically but is reflected in all true science in such a wonderful way that the assumed fact of an eternally existing triune God is an inductive necessity before the universe, as science knows it today, can be explained at all.

The doctrine of the Trinity is nowhere set forth in the Bible as an explicit doctrine. Rather, it appears indirectly, and yet perfectly naturally, as Jesus speaks of Himself and of the Father and of the Holy Spirit. Always the logical, causal order presented is: first, God the Father—the unseen source and cause of all things; second, God the Son—who tangibly and visibly reveals the Father to man and who executes the will of God; third, God the Holy Spirit—who is unseen and yet reveals God the Son to men through the media of other men and the Word which He inspired, and who makes real in the hearts and lives of men the experience of fellowship with the Son and the Father. Yet this is not an order of importance or length of existence. All are equally eternal and equally God —one God. The Son is presented as "begotten of the Father," the Spirit as proceeding from the Father through the Son.

Now consider the physical universe which logically should reflect in a very intimate way its Creator. All knowable things in this universe may be classified under the heads of space, matter or time. Now space, at least as far as we can comprehend it, consists of exactly three dimensions, each equally important and absolutely essential. There would be no space, no reality, if there were only two dimensions. Three distinct dimensions exist, yet each comprises the whole of space. Yet there is just one space. Note that to get the cubical contents of any certain confined space, one does not add the length and breadth and width, but rather multiplies them together. Analogously, the mathematics of the Trinity is not $1 + 1 + 1 = 1$, but $1 \times 1 \times 1 = 1$.

The analogy is even more striking in matter. The new physics has come to regard matter more and more as "simply" tremendous energy in motion. Depending on the rates and types of motion, there are then various phenomena presented to our senses—sound, color, heat, texture, hardness, etc. Energy is the unseen source manifesting itself in motion and thus producing phenomena. Matter involves these three phases and no others that cannot rightly be included in one of these. Each is distinct, yet each involves the whole of matter, and none of the three can exist by itself without the other two. Energy is first in a logical, causal order, but not in order of importance or precedence. Motion, which embodies, reveals and is begotten of energy, is the second. Phenomena proceed from motion and comprise the ways in which motion itself touches and affects men, even as the Holy Spirit reveals the Son and, through Him, the Father to men.

Finally, the last of the triad, time, is one entity but consists of the future, the present and the past. Each contains the whole of time, yet is distinct and, further, cannot exist without the other two. The future is the unseen source of time and is embodied and made real, moment by moment, in the present. The past then proceeds from the present, becoming invisible again, yet continually influencing us with regard to the present and even, to some extent, the future.

Furthermore, the three basic entities unite to form the space-mass-time continuum which constitutes the physical cosmos itself. Space is the invisible, omnipresent background, manifest everywhere in matter (or more generally, energy), interpreted and experienced through time. Thus the physical universe is actually a trinity of trinities, a triuniverse in the fullest sense.

But this same remarkable phenomenon can be seen in the realm of human life as well. The Bible says that man was created in the image of God, so this should be expected.

Notice that each individual is a person who can be physically observed and described. But back of that person is his nature, which is unseen and yet is the source of all that the person embodies. But that person, and through the person his nature, is known to other men only through his personality, which is an unseen, intangible thing, yet the means by which the person touches the lives of others. So human life consists of three things—nature, person and personality—and no others. Although they are equally important and equally the whole of the man, yet they always exist in the above logical order. None of the three can exist without the other two. The nature is the source, revealed and embodied in the person. The personality proceeds from the person. It is invisible but is felt by and has influence on the lives of others in regard to the person. Thus man is, in minute detail, a finite reflection of God who made him in His own image. It is true that sin has marred even this finite reflection, nevertheless man still reflects the image of God in an even more significant way than does the physical universe.

This same trinity seems to pervade everything in life. Every moral action of man consists of: first, the motive; second, the act; third, the consequences. The same relations apply among these as among the triunities we have already mentioned. Similarly, all forms of thought or reason proceed logically from the universal to the particular thing to that thing as related to other things.

This triunity of source, manifestation and meaning could be further noted in many other areas of the world and life. But even this brief discussion should suffice to indicate something of the basic system of three-in-oneness pervading the whole creation. While these facts cannot be held to *prove* that the Creator of the universe and of life is a triune Being, it should be obvious that such a cause would be eminently adequate to account for all these facts. It is certainly difficult and perhaps impossible to formulate any other hypothesis as satisfactory as this to account for the existence of such universal triunity in nature. The doctrine of the Trinity is no unscientific, aboriginal absurdity, but an intensely scientific and tremendously important living reality. God was manifested and revealed by and in His Son, who as a man was Jesus Christ. There can be nothing more important for any individual then, than to become rightly related to this triuniverse and its triune God. This means unreserved acceptance of Christ, for "in him dwelleth all the fulness of the Godhead bodily" (Col. 2:9).

2

THE THEORY OF EVOLUTION

IT IS A SERIOUS MISTAKE to ignore, as many Christians seem willing to do, the tremendous implications and influence of the theory of evolution. By far the majority of college-trained men and women have been taught to accept evolution as a demonstrated fact of science, and it is being taught increasingly in the high schools and even the grade schools of the country. It has probably contributed more to the prevalent secularistic and materialistic philosophy of the world today than any other one influence. Obviously, something that is so important ought to be seriously studied by all thinking men and women. On the other hand, very few people have actually had the opportunity to study the great mass of evidence against the theory, and in fact would usually be found to be quite ignorant of the fact that very powerful contrary scientific evidence does exist.

For that matter, evolution is not so much a science as it is a philosophy or an attitude of mind. Evolutionists admit that evolution requires aeons of time in which to work and that the paltry few thousand years of written records that are available to us do not reveal one real example of genuine evolution taking place. And since no one was present to watch the supposed great evolutionary changes of the past, it is manifestly impossible to prove scientifically that they actually did take place.

Furthermore, the fundamental principle of evolution

—the concept of development, with increasing organization and complexity—seems to be essentially contradictory to the impregnably established laws of energy conservation and deterioration. These laws affirm the fact that creation of matter or energy is not now taking place, and, in fact, that the available energy of the universe as a whole is continually running down rather than building up. Therefore, it seems evident that the creation of the universe and its components must have been accomplished and completed by means of processes which are no longer in force, and which therefore cannot be observed and studied at the present time. The Bible, of course, also teaches the fact of a creation *already completed* by God, as revealed especially in Genesis 1.

The theory of evolution, on the other hand, is essentially an attempt to explain the origin of all things in terms of processes which are still continuing and which therefore can still be studied in the present. It therefore ignores the Bible's witness to a *completed* creation, and assumes that creation is still going on (if one may call the process of evolution by the term "creation"). The history of "creation" that is built up by a study of the physical and biological processes that now prevail in the world must quite obviously, therefore, differ widely from the history of creation as revealed by God in the Bible, not only in principle but also in its details.

Evolutionary geology propounds that living organisms originated in the sea, countless millions of years before plants or any other forms of life appeared on the land. Genesis, however, states clearly that grasses, seed-bearing herbs, and fruit trees were created on the third day, and that water animals (and land animals and birds, as well) were not brought into existence until the fifth day. The Bible states that birds were created on the same day as the fish and other marine creatures. Evolution, however, teaches that birds were evolved from reptiles long after the origin of the fish and probably even after the first appearance of mammals. According to Scripture, the "creeping things" (especially insects, see Lev. 11:20-23) were among the last things created, coincident with the land animals and reptiles. According to evolution, insects appeared very early, reaching their greatest development even before the first appearance of reptiles, birds and mammals.

The great lights for ruling the day and the night were not set at these functions until the fourth day, which would certainly be quite lethal to the vegetation created on the third day, if these days were longer than twenty-four hours. Further, the use of the words "evening" and "morning" as describing the beginning and end of each day, certainly would imply ordinary days as we know them. Some have made much of the fact that the Hebrew word translated "day" may sometimes be used to indicate a long, indefinite period of time. This is true, but it is also true that in the overwhelming majority of cases it refers to a twenty-four-hour period, and that wherever it is used with an ordinal (first, second, etc.) as it is here, it *always* refers to a twenty-four-hour day.

Another difficulty with the day-age idea is that the Bible says that death entered the world as a result of the sin of the first man and woman. However, if these days can be taken as long ages, as pictured by some geologists, the bones of dead millions of God's creatures were in the ground before man was even on the scene. Also, with such evidence of death and suffering prevailing throughout the world, why would God have pronounced His completed creation "very good," as He is said to have done in the last verse of Genesis 1? Finally, God instituted the Sabbath as a memorial of His completed work. As far back as any records go, mankind has been observing every seventh day as a day of rest. This is difficult to explain unless God did actually rest from His work on the seventh literal day of creation. In Exodus 20:11, in incorporating the observance of the Sabbath into the law of Israel, and just after saying in verse 10 that "the seventh day is the sabbath of the LORD thy God," the following statement appears: "For in *six days* the LORD made heaven and earth, the sea, and *all that in them is,* and rested the seventh day: wherefore the LORD blessed the seventh day, and hallowed it." The explanatory argument for this command would have no force if the basis of man's workweek and Sabbath rest was not an exactly equivalent workweek and Sabbath rest experienced by the Creator. Furthermore, the Hebrew word translated "days" in this passage (Exodus 20:8-11) is used twice, once for the six workdays of God, once for the six workdays of man. The word is *never* used elsewhere in the Old Testament to mean anything other than literal days, although it occurs more than seven hundred times. It is well also to note that there is at least one good Hebrew word meaning "age" or "long, indefinite time," which could have been used here and in the Genesis account if that meaning had been in the mind of the writer. The fact that he used the words "day" and "days" without any intimation that he was using them in a symbolic sense, makes it very evident that the literal meaning was intended.

Even if it were possible to regard the story of the creation as a beautiful but unhistorical allegory, striking difficulties would appear at later parts in the Bible. Time and again throughout the Old Testament, reference is made by the various writers to the creation and to Adam and to the other characters connected with the Genesis story, always with the obvious belief on the part of the writer that he is speaking of definite historical characters and events. This is true even in the New Testament. Paul, intellectually one of the greatest men who ever lived as well as one of the greatest Christians, refers again and again to the creation and fall of man. In fact, the fall of Adam and the resultant entering of sin into the world is one of the basic doctrines of Christian theology as presented by Paul. He emphasizes the fact that all men are sinners by nature because of the sin of the first man, Adam, and that it is only through the last Adam, Jesus Christ, that man can be freed from the penalties and consequences of sin (see Rom. 5:12-19). Evolution, on the other hand, does not concede that man ever fell, but avers that he has gradually risen from the state of the beast and is getting better all the time. Any evil that is in him is not sin inherited from his father, Adam, but simply beastly instincts that are a holdover from his simian ancestors.

Even Jesus Christ believed in the Genesis record of creation. In Matthew 19:3-6, we read: "The Pharisees also came unto him, tempting him, and saying unto him, Is it lawful for a man to put away his wife for every cause? And he answered and said unto them, Have ye not read, that he which made them at the beginning made them male and female, and said, For this cause shall a man leave father and mother, and shall cleave to his wife: and they twain shall be one flesh? . . . What therefore God hath joined together, let not man put asunder." Certainly, if Jesus really was the Son of God, as He claimed to be, He would not have based His teaching about an important institution like marriage on a mythical or legendary event.

It is thus absolutely impossible to believe in the Bible as the complete and literal Word of God and to believe in the theory of evolution. But, more than that, it is almost impossible to believe in a personal God of any sort if one believes in evolution. The so-called theistic evolutionists, who manage to think of evolution as "God's method of creation," and who profess to see in evolution a grand and beautiful and orderly process of nature—one that enlarges and develops one's conception of God—are being inexcusably inconsistent. Evolution, by its very nature, is materialistic; it is nothing but an attempt to explain the facts of biology in terms of laws of nature without the necessity of recourse to the idea of the supernatural or the divine. Mechanism and the doctrine of chance constitute the very quintessence of evolution.

If God actually did create the universe, including all living creatures, by the method of evolution, it appears to this writer that He must have selected the most inefficient and cruel and foolish method of doing it that one can imagine. If His goal was the creation of man, what possible reason could there have been for such misfits as dinosaurs to rule and roam the earth for millions of years, only to die out long before man arrived on the scene? Evolution is supposed to have come about by means of the struggle for existence and the survival of the fittest, which, if true, would mean that God deliberately instituted a law that would have depended for its enforcement on the credo that might is right and that the strong should exterminate the weak. Millions of animals must have perished in the course of the evolutionary process for no conceivable reason if, as the modernists assert, man was the ultimate goal of it all. As one atheist professor puts it: "The whole history of evolution reveals and witnesses that there is no intelligence back of the process. You cannot understand evolution and believe in God."

Furthermore, the atheistic and satanic character of the doctrine is evidenced in the many evil social doctrines it has spawned. Nietzsche and Marx, both radically atheistic, were profoundly influenced by the

Darwinian ideas of natural selection and the survival of the fittest. They carried into the social and philosophic realms what Darwin had attempted to apply to the biological realm, and concocted their deadly philosophies. From Marx, the world has inherited socialism, communism, and anarchism. Nietzsche's philosophy profoundly influenced German political thought and became the basis of the intense German militarism of the past century. Mussolini was a most zealous disciple of Nietzsche, and Fascism was the result. Nazism was bred in the same cesspool. Evolution is also the basis of the many types of immoral doctrines taught in the psychological fields by Freud, Russell and others. The gospels of gloom known as determinism and behaviorism and existentialism have the same foundation.

It seems unthinkable that a theory of any kind could have had such far-reaching and such deadly effects as has the theory of evolution. By the very fact of goodness and beauty in the world, it is hard to believe that such a theory could really be true. And yet, one may say, if science has proved that it is true, then we shall have to accept it regardless of the implications. That may be so, but we should certainly demand the most rigid and unquestionable proof before receiving such a godless theory as proved fact. The purpose of this chapter is to make a brief survey of the so-called proofs that have thus far been offered by the evolutionists.

Organic evolution, as usually defined, means the gradual development of all forms of life by natural processes from a common ancestral form, which itself had arisen by natural processes from complex chemicals in the earth's primeval ocean. From such primitive self-reproducing chemical substances, single-celled organisms developed, and from these evolved plants and multicelled invertebrates. Then came fishes and insects, later amphibians and reptiles, then birds and mammals, and finally man.

But there is an overwhelming scientific objection right at the beginning, namely, the impossibility of accounting for the development of living organisms from nonliving chemicals in the first place. The notion of "spontaneous generation" was widely held until demolished by Pasteur and others a hundred years ago. It is known beyond doubt that there is no such process occurring in the present world, even though countless numbers of experiments have been made to discover or develop such a process. Thus the evolutionist has to resort to an explanation in terms of an imaginary atmosphere which no longer exists, an imaginary ocean composition which no longer exists, and hypothetical processes which no longer exist, to explain the evolution of primitive organisms which no longer exist! Whatever philosophic or religious value such speculations might have, they are certainly not *scientific*.

Even if modern biochemists eventually are able to synthesize the intricately complex self-replicating nucleic acids which exist in all living protoplasm, from their basic chemical elements (a highly improbable, but perhaps not impossible, accomplishment), this will still be far short of creating even the simplest living cell. Nor would it by any means prove that life originally developed by such processes occurring spontaneously, without benefit of hundreds of highly trained scientists and millions of dollars of federal research grants to stimulate them.

The feverish modern search for even the slightest trace of life on other planets reflects the wistful hope that an evolutionary theory of life will somehow be vindicated by such a discovery. If the solar system, and indeed the entire universe, can be understood in terms of cosmic and chemical evolution, and if the evolution of living materials has a physicochemical basis, then of course there is no reason why life should not have similarly appeared on other planets. As yet, however, despite the space probes, giant telescopes, and even the UFO furor, there is not the slightest genuine evidence of biological life as we understand it anywhere else in the universe.

The fact that all living flesh is fundamentally composed of the simple chemical elements found in the earth is of course further confirmation of Scripture, which clearly states that both plant life (Gen. 1:11-12) and animal life (Gen. 1:20, 24) were "brought forth" from the earth and its waters, and that even man's body was formed of the "dust of the earth" (Gen. 2:7). However, the fact that there was also a life-principle not inherent in these basic substances is also stressed in the case of both animals ("living creatures," Gen. 1:24) and man ("living soul"—same words in the original Hebrew as "living creature" in Gen. 2:7), and there is not the slightest evidence that modern scientists will ever be able to synthesize anything corresponding to a "living soul," nor that such was ever accomplished by natural processes in the earth's prehistoric ages.

But, of course, from the standpoint of the evolutionist, it is quite necessary to insist on some form of spontaneous generation, as that is the only way life can be accounted for apart from a Creator. If God were to be admitted at any part of the process, it is far more consistent with the concept of His power and efficiency, and certainly that of His grace and mercy, to suppose that He would have created the earth and its living creatures fully developed and functioning from the beginning.

Not only does the theory fail to account for the origin of life, but it cannot even provide a satisfactory explanation of the method by which evolution works.

A great many proposed explanations have been offered by a great many investigators and theorizers, but the mechanics of evolution remains just as mysterious as it was a hundred years ago. Many modern biologists frankly admit their ignorance of this most important phase of their theory.

The first important suggestion offered was Lamarck's theory of the transmissibility of characters acquired through the effects of environment or other external influences. The theory has been utterly disproved both by experiment and by the advance in genetic theory; so it need not detain us here.

Much the same dictum of complete rejection could be pronounced upon the Darwinian theory of natural selection. According to Darwin's idea, the endless varieties and individual differences that are observed to occur among different members of the same species make occasional individuals better fitted to survive in the struggle for existence. These individuals then persist and transmit these favorable characteristics to their descendants, while others less fortunate gradually are eliminated. Infinite accumulations of these favorable hereditable variations are invoked to account for the gradual formation of all forms of life. Plausible as all this may sound, however, more detailed studies and knowledge of the specific and germinal characters of plants and animals has made it clear that natural selection alone cannot account for the origin of species. In the first place, it cannot account for the origin of the very necessary variations. The rediscovered Mendelian laws of heredity, which were apparently unknown to Darwin and the other founders of evolution, showed that all these chance variations followed definite, though frequently quite complicated, arithmetical laws. They showed that, except under very extraordinary circumstances not usually occurring in nature, all variation was within certain fixed limits and that no hereditable characteristic could appear in an individual that had not existed in one, at least, of his parents (that characteristic may have been "dormant" or not appearing in the parent or even in several generations of ancestors, but was nevertheless present germinally).

The countless experiments which have verified Mendel's laws have in recent years been further substantiated by increased knowledge of the character of living cells. It is now known that all cells are not the same, but are fundamentally and definitely different among the various species. Even in the same creature, the cells composing different parts of the body are clearly distinct. Each cell contains a number of component parts, only one of which, though probably the most important, is protoplasm. From the standpoint of genetics and heredity, the most interesting parts of the cell are the chromosomes, which are known, from a study or the activity of the cells in reproduction, to be the carrier of heredity. Each chromosome is a threadlike structure and there is a definite number of them in each cell of the creature. This is true regardless of the part of the body in which that cell is located. The number of chromosomes in each cell depends entirely upon the species in which the cells are found; for example, human cells contain forty-six chromosomes. However, the germ cells of each species contain only half the usual number of chromosomes for the species, so that when the chromosomes of the male and female germ cells unite, a new cell will be formed that contains the correct number of chromosomes for the species.

In order to explain theoretically the laws of heredity discovered by Mendel, the gene theory has been developed. According to this theory, each chromosome is composed of a large number of entities called genes. Each gene is supposed to govern or control some characteristic in the individual. Also, various combinations of genes may influence characteristics. Recombinations, shufflings, etc., of genes can thus be invoked to account mathematically for all the fixed and variable characters that are observed in members of a species. It is now believed that each gene is a part of a very complex molecule of deoxyribose nucleic acid (DNA), the detailed structure of which is "coded" to build the particular character which it controls in the organism. This code is transmitted very faithfully and accurately from the genetic systems of the parents. Thus, although extensive variation is possible because of the many possible combinations of genetic factors, it must always be within the ancestral limits imposed by the genetic code for the particular kind of organism. All of the small chance variations which are supposedly acted upon by natural selection to form new species are really nothing but new combinations of genetic factors, which were already in the parent or parents in the first place. Thus nothing new is added, and variation is held within fixed limits and tends to hover about a certain mean which has proved, by experience in nature, to be the best for the particular species concerned. Thus, natural selection, instead of tending to produce new species, really acts to preserve those already in existence.

Furthermore, natural selection by its very nature requires an almost infinite number of transitional forms in the origin of a new species. But this is not borne out by the fossil record which in most cases reveals only very distinct forms. There are very few intermediate forms between established genera found either in living forms or in the fossils. There are practically none between the families and comparatively few even between the species as ordinarily defined. These facts have led most evolutionists to conclude that evolution occurs, not by accumulations of small variations, but rather by means of sudden, relatively large genetic changes called mutations. This conclusion appeared to be necessary, not only by virtue of the discontinuous nature of the fossil record, but also because modern genetic theory had shown that all normal inheritance and variation followed the Mendelian laws and was strictly circumscribed.

The mutation theory was largely developed by Hugo DeVries, in his work on the evening primrose, and T. H. Morgan, experimenting with the fruit fly. These and other workers observed that a distinctly new characteristic would sometimes suddenly appear in an individual. This change was called a mutation and it was found that the new character was hereditable and that it followed the Mendelian laws. Mutations were attributed to actual changes in the chromosomes or genes of the germ cells and have now become probably the most popular present-day means of explaining evolution. It is usually stated that when mutations occur they are then acted upon by natural selection and, if helpful in the struggle for existence, they will tend to survive and thus gradually form a new species.

In terms of the genetic code, a mutation is regarded as a "mistake" in transmission of heredity information, caused by a random change in the DNA molecular structure. However, mutations are very rare as the code is ordinarily highly stable. In addition, it is probable that many supposed mutations are merely ordinary variations which had no opportunity for expression in the population until the right parents happened to come together or until a changed environment permitted the establishment of a previously dormant variety. Furthermore, true mutations occur comparatively rarely in nature and, when they do occur, they usually tend to disappear. This is because all genuine mutations that have thus far been observed are of either a pathologic or a neutral character. Never does a mutation seem to be in the least degree beneficial. Most of the laboratory mutations have been induced artifically by chemicals, heat, X rays, ultraviolet rays, etc. Furthermore, these mutations are almost always recessive when crossed back with the original type. That is another reason why they will not persist in nature. When one considers the great odds against a mutation's being helpful and surviving in the struggle for existence and then realizes that the formation of a new species would require not one mutation but thousands, and finally considers the tremendous number of species of plants and animals in the world, it would seem to demand a most amazing credulity to imagine that here is the method by which evolution takes place. And yet that is precisely what is taught as gospel truth in probably the majority of schools today.

As a result, there are hundreds of qualified scientists today who reject evolution altogether. Even many evolutionists believe that such mutations as have actually been observed are apparently of an entirely different order from those which would be required for genuine evolution to occur. These mutations have been called "micromutations" to indicate their relatively small magnitude and significance. The much larger mutations that seem to be demanded by both the fossil record and genetic theory have been called "macromutations," "systemic mutations," "saltational mutations," and similar terms. This sort of mutation has not been observed experimentally, of course, and seems impossible to account for on the basis of genetic theory itself, not to mention its implied contravention of the basic laws of energy fransformation. The Neo-Darwinians, who still accept micromutations as the main basis of evolution, are forced to account for the great "gaps" in terms of hypothetical periods of accelerated or "explosive" evolution.

The fact that the majority of men in these fields

continue to believe in evolution would seem to result largely from the supposed external proofs of evolution. We can consider only the most important of these proofs—those that appear most often in textbooks. None of them is conclusive or convincing.

Comparative anatomy is appealed to, for one thing. The anatomical and physiological resemblances between different species are considered, for some reason, evidence of relationship. For example, the general structural similarity between man and the ape, or between any other two mammals, for that matter, is cited as proof of kinship. As a matter of fact, the structural differences between species are of as great significance as the more or less superficial similarities. Anyway what does similarity of structure prove other than a common plan of creation, modified in details to meet specific needs? That would be the logical thing to expect on the hypothesis of special creation. The skeletal framework of every vertebrate is a model of design, especially arranged to accommodate the creature using it. The marvelous efficiency and ingenious construction of the skeleton is of especial appeal to the engineer interested in structural designing. It is safe to say that no building or bridge or any other engineering structure ever built could compare in excellence of design to the structural framework of the lowliest animal. Since all mammals, as well as man, have somewhat the same physical functions, it is only natural that the equipment for those functions should be similar.

The old argument from vestigial organs is still occasionally mentioned in textbooks. According to this idea, certain supposedly useless organs in man, such as the appendix, the ductless glands, the coccyx, etc., are vestiges of useful organs in lower animals, hanging over from man's former animal existence. At one time there were supposed to be 180 of these organs in man.

However, as ignorance was replaced by knowledge of the use of these so-called useless organs, the number rapidly dwindled until now most evolutionists would not claim any. Such organs as may truly be useless in various creatures would, it would seem, be poor evidence of evolution anyway. They are probably the results of mutational changes which, as we have seen, are usually deteriorations.

Another proffered line of evidence was the recapitulation theory which taught that the embryonic development of any organism was a condensed recapitulation of the past evolutionary development of that organism. This theory, first vigorously promulgated by Haeckel, precipitated much embryologic study, engaged in mainly for the purpose of building up philogenies (evolutionary history) for different creatures.

Further paleontologic, embryologic and biochemical investigations have dealt so hardly with the theory that it has been quite generally discarded as a useful tool in embryologic or geologic research. Comparisons of many ontogenies (embryonic developments) with their supposed corresponding philogenies as indicated by expanding paleontologic data, have revealed innumerable omissions, additions, accelerations, retardations, oversteppings, etc. Consequently, the theory has come to be regarded probably by most serious embryologists as incorrect, though they nevertheless often choose to regard embryonic development in an evolutionary perspective. In any case, there is surely no justification for offering such a theory as "proof" of evolution.

In the very early stages of the development of an embryo, there are many similarities among embryos of different species or even of different families. All embryos start from a microscopic germ cell and of necessity must develop along similar lines for a time, so such resemblances are only to be expected and are no indication of any genetic relationship. However, after about a month, each type of embryo is visually distinguishable from those of other creatures. Even before this, at any time after conception, an examination of the embryo's cell structure would of course unfailingly reveal its true character.

As a matter of fact, much evidence has been accumulated by qualified scientists that *every* stage in the development of every embryo that has been so studied is *quite necessary to the most efficient development of that embryo.* The marvelous embryonic growth of all living creatures at every step, instead of supporting evolution, actually offers abundant testimony to a great Designer and does not in any way give countenance to theories of materialistic origin and development.

Evidences for evolution based essentially on similarity, such as these from comparative anatomy and embryology, as well as those from similarities in blood serum and other biochemical and physiological properties of organisms, and even from the very fact that creatures can be classified into groups of different degrees of similarity, all assume the very point that needs to be proved, namely, that similarity implies relationship. All such similarities, however, are more reasonably explained in terms of origin at the hand of a common Designer.

It is well to observe at this point that the Bible does not teach the fixity of species, and for the simple reason that no one knows just what a species is. Few issues are more alive among biologists today than this matter of what constitutes a species. Certainly, according to many definitions of the term, many new species have been "evolved" since the original creation. Genetic research has proved conclusively that chromosome changes, gene mutations, and hybridization can produce and, in fact, have produced many distinctly new varieties, in both plants and animals. These varieties are often considered new species, or even genera, by most modern methods of classification.

However, all evidence thus far in the genetic field seems to prove conclusively that these agencies of change cannot go beyond certain comparatively narrow limits and can very definitely not produce new "kinds." The Genesis account merely says that each created group was to produce "after its kind," with no clear indication as to what constitutes a "kind," except the implication that different kinds would not be interfertile (if they were, they would not be reproducing after their respective kinds). Thus, the biblical account leaves ample room for just such conditions of change within the smaller groups and stability within the larger groups as is indicated by modern discovery.

We cannot be sure just what today constitutes a "kind," with the one exception of the man "kind." As all experience and evidence has conclusively proved, man cannot cross with any other creature in the earth, although all the very different races of men are freely interfertile. Furthermore, there are very definite limits of crossing between the groups which in modern taxonomy are called genera, with seemingly no crosses among the families.

It is probable that the original Genesis "kind" is sometimes equivalent to our modern species, sometimes to the genus, and perhaps in some instances to the family. In any case, there is not the slightest evidence that evolution ever has occurred or ever can occur across the "kinds."

Finally then, the only real factual data upon which the evolutionary hypothesis rests are provided in the fossil record, which we shall now examine briefly.

The statement is frequently made in textbooks that the fossils as found in the sedimentary rocks of the world always indicate evolution. That is, in the lower strata, only simple and unspecialized forms are found; then as the surface is approached, increasingly high and complex types appear. This gradual increase in size and complexity of the fossils has, in fact, served as the main basis of identifying the various geologic strata and correlating them from place to place. The time during which these strata have been deposited is believed to extend over hundreds of millions of years. All of this is considered to be strong proof that evolution *has* occurred in the past, even though we may not now understand its mechanism.

There are a number of serious difficulties with the geological time scale and with the evolutionary interpretations placed upon the fossils in the rocks by paleontologists and historical geologists. Some of these problems are considered in the next chapter.

However, even if we assume for the sake of argument that the geologic time scale is trustworthy, several facts appear which are convincing evidence against evolution. Some of these might be enumerated briefly as follows:

1. Many, many species have remained absolutely fixed through all the supposed millions and millions of years of geologic time. Many such are now known and it is certain that many more would be recognized if it were not for the somewhat dishonest habit paleontologists have of giving new names to all species found as fossils regardless of how closely they resemble living species. Among the creatures that have thus remained unchanged through all the course of evolutionary history are the very protozoa with which evolution is supposed to have begun. This is difficult to understand if evolution is the universal law of nature.

2. A great many modern species are very evidently degenerate, rather than higher, forms of those

that are found as fossils. These would include practically all mammals—elephants, tigers, wolves, apes, lions, rhinos, hippos, bears, beavers, etc. It is also true of multitudes of plants of all kinds, as well as insects, birds, fishes, amphibians and reptiles (compare the dinosaurs to our modern snakes and alligators). Some evolution!

3. All of the great phyla and most of the families, orders and classes, as well as very many genera and even species, appear quite suddenly in the fossil record, with no preliminary or intermediate forms.

It would be well, however, to consider a few of the more publicized paleontological proofs of evolution, since these "proofs" are usually those that sound most impressive to the average student. The famous case of the horse is, without doubt, the most noteworthy of these demonstrations and according to the evolutionists' own claims is the best proof evolution has.

At the very most, the horse pedigree usually drawn up in popular evolutionary textbooks does not prove evolution across family boundaries, but only within the family. The very earliest member, *Eohippus,* is quite obviously as much a member of the horse family as the living *Equus. Eohippus* was small, about the size of a fox, with four toes on the front foot and three on the hind. The modern horse, of course, has only one toe on each foot, with possible vestiges of others. There are other minor differences between *Eohippus* and *Equus,* which, however, are mainly adaptations (or designs) as a result of their difference in size. Between these two genera have been ranged about a dozen others, found as fossils. Some of these had the same toe arrangements as *Eohippus,* some had three toes on each foot, and still others have the side toes reduced to splints as in the modern horse.

However, all these animals are said to have lived

in the Tertiary, late in geologic time. They are found near the surface, in the relatively unconsolidated Tertiary deposits. The different forms are not found superimposed one over the other, but at widely separated localities, often continents apart. No gradual evolution from one to the other is evident, but only a series of sudden jumps at best.

There is, further, no clue to the origin of *Eohippus,* who was as highly developed, specialized, and fitted to his environment as is the modern horse. All things considered, it seems quite as plausible to say that each of the several genera may have been living simultaneously, perhaps as mutant variants of the originally created horse kind, and that they, in common with many other zoological inhabitants of a former age, have for one reason or another since become extinct.

Even if one of these forms actually should prove to be the ancestor of the modern horse (and such has not yet been proved by any means), the loss of one or more toes is obviously to be attributed to a mutation, and in common with all known mutations is in the nature of a deterioration rather than an advance. As to size, it is obvious that there are many families in the present world containing members differing in size quite as much as *Eohippus* and *Equus.* Furthermore, many fossil horses have been found in many regions, fully as large and sometimes larger than the modern horse. Many of them seem, in fact, quite identical with *Equus,* though others have three toes and other differences.

All things considered, this supposed best demonstration of evolution falls more than somewhat short of being such a demonstration at all. And the same sort of criticisms could be brought against the supposed evolutionary pedigrees of the camel, the elephant, and other animals, which are sometimes, but with less confidence, offered as evidence in popular textbooks.

There remains then the problem of the fossil men that have been classed as prehuman. These bear especially hard on our belief in the Bible story of man's creation and so are particularly interesting.

The evolutionary reconstructions one sees in museums are very impressive but are highly imaginative and speculative. There has never yet been found a complete skeleton, or even a complete skull, of an ape-man or man-ape, although large numbers of remains of true apes and true men have been found. Only a few bone fragments have been found which could be imagined into any sort of lower species of man, a strange situation in view of the multiplied millions of ape-men that must have lived and died during the course of evolutionary history. But there is no scarcity of theories and there are numerous schools of thought today among anthropologists as to where the various fossils of protomen fit into the assumed history of human evolution.

The most notorious of all is the famous Pithecanthropus Erectus, found in Java in 1891 and 1892. This find consisted of a part of a skullcap, a fragment of a left thighbone and three molar teeth. These parts were not found together but within a range of some fifty feet. They were not found at the same time but within the space of a year apart. They were found in an old riverbed, far below high watermark, mingled with much debris and many bones of extinct animals.

In recent years there have been other finds in Java which have affected the status of Pithecanthropus, so that he is now regarded by most present-day anthropologists as essentially identical with modern man. The original skull has come to be regarded as that of a small woman. The femur is admittedly completely human in form. The teeth were probably simian and did not belong with the other remains at all.

The Neanderthal race of cavemen has been more

widely publicized perhaps than any other of these ancient men, except possibly Pithecanthropus. The original Neanderthal Man consisted of a skullcap, which was attested by various experts to be that of an ape man, a Negro, an idiot, a modern Cossack, an early German, and several other things. Since that time, a number of other skeletons and fragments have been found in Europe and at other points around the Mediterranean. Many of these are very questionable, but some evidently belonged to the Neanderthal Race, which is now acknowledged by probably the majority of paleontologists to be identical in species with modern man. Fairly frequently perfect Neanderthal types appear among modern peoples. It seems most probable that the Neanderthals represented a degenerate, rather than a developing, race.

The Peking Man is represented by quite a number of individuals found in caves near Peking, China, the first in 1929. This was also first acclaimed as an important "missing link." With the discovery of more remains, however, it has been found that some of them are quite modern. Others are similar to the Neanderthal type, and there are none of the skeletal features which cannot be duplicated in modern races or individuals.

In recent years much attention has been centered on the various fossils found in South Africa by Dart, Broom and Leakey. Most of these are grouped under the name Australopithecines, and some are dated as much as three million years ago. Although some of their features have been assumed to be prehuman, they nevertheless were probably true men. There is much evidence that they fashioned and used tools and weapons, as well as fire. It is interesting that the oldest of these men, *Homo Habilis,* is also most nearly like modern man. Except for his small size, he could very well pass for a modern man.

It is significant that these and other fossil protomen are individually represented only by small fragments of bone and also that all are dated within the Pleistocene Epoch. However, the unknown hypothetical common ancestor of apes and men is dated in the Eocene, about seventy million years earlier, with all the intermediate forms still missing.

There are others that might be discussed, but those already mentioned are the best known and are supposed to provide the best evidence for human evolution. This whole subject seems replete with varying opinions and ever changing interpretations on the part of the different experts involved. The past sixty or so years have even witnessed a number of outright boners on the part of several such authorities, such as the elephant's kneebone discovered in Java in 1926, acclaimed for some time as a new skull of Pithecanthropus. Then there was the Hesperopithecus tooth found in 1922 in Nebraska, which was accepted so widely as evidence of man's antiquity that it was introduced by the evolutionists as expert testimony in the famous "evolution trial" in Tennessee in 1925. Two years later, however, the complete skeleton was found and proved rather to have belonged to an extinct pig. The so-called Colorado Man (also constructed from a tooth) was later found to have belonged to the horse family. An ape-man skull, also found in Colorado, exhibited as such for a time in a museum, was actually the skull of a pet monkey buried a few years previously. A bone found near Seattle, identified as an ancient human fibula, turned out to be part of a bear's hind leg. Finally, the famous Piltdown Man, regarded until recently as one of the three or four most important of the "missing links" in man's evolution, has now been formally pronounced to have been a clever hoax which fooled all the anthropological specialists for forty years before being exposed.

It is of great significance that many fossilized skeletons of modern man have been found at many different locations, and often with every indication of being as old or older than the supposedly less advanced hominids that have been unearthed. Some of the more famous of these include the Men of Swanscombe, Galley Hill, Grimaldi, Oldoway, Foxhall, Wadjak, Fontechevade, and others—all of whom are practically indistinguishable from modern man and which yet give evidence of at least as great geologic age as any of the other presumably more primitive types. Some of the outstanding present-day anthropologists have therefore adopted the theory that modern man existed contemporaneously with Neanderthal man, and the others, and that all represent variant races evolved from some as-yet-undiscovered ancestor.

On the other hand, there is no real evidence against the far more reasonable theory, adopted by some, that the Neanderthals, Peking Man, etc., represent degenerate races, descended from Homo Sapiens as a result of mutation, isolation, etc. In fact, there is some evidence that modern man himself is a somewhat deteriorated descendant of his ancestors. The Cro-Magnon race of men, who inhabited Europe about the same time as the Neanderthals, are well known to have been superior to modern man, both in physical size and in brain capacity.

Since practically nothing is really known about the actual physiologic characteristics and physical appearance of any of these protomen, there is no reason why the Australopithecines and the Pithecanthropines (or Homo Erectus, as they are also called), as well as the Neanderthals and others, could not be regarded as extinct races of mankind, all descendants of Adam. Considering the wide variety of present-day human types, the slight additional differences indicated by the fossils would seem to be well within the range of potential genetic variation and mutation for man.

These facts serve to add emphasis to a principle already alluded to several times, namely, that developmental evolution is *not* the universal law of biology, but rather deterioration or degeneration. As we have seen, there is no real evidence of progressive evolution, but very much evidence for deteriorative evolution or, at best, biologic stability.

We have already seen, in the previous chapter, that this law of degeneration, or entropy increase, is universally operative throughout the physical and chemical realms; it now seems also to pervade the biologic realm. In fact, this truth is beginning so to disturb evolutionists that several significant papers have appeared recently in scientific journals, attempting to harmonize the concept of evolution with the second law of thermodynamics, but with no real success.

More and more it appears that there is one great degenerative principle pervading all nature, of which the law of entropy is merely its special manifestation in physical phenomena. This law has been called by Dr. R. E. D. Clark the "law of morpholysis" (morpholysis means "loosing of structure"). In other words, there is a universal tendency from the highly organized to the disorganized, from the ordered to the disordered. Never is there an inherent, natural, undirected, unaided, trend toward increase of order or organization. The natural tendency is always downward.

In biology an important example is found in the very agencies supposed to bring about evolution, that is, gene mutations and chromosome changes or aberrations. All such changes are harmful or at best indifferent, as far as the organism is concerned. They seem clearly to represent a breaking down of the original ordered arrangement of the genes in the germ cells, brought about through penetration of the germ cell by X rays, cosmic radiation, or some other disorganizing medium. In some way the genetic structure is disarranged and since if the mutations are not actually lethal they are both harmful and hereditary, the eventual result is a deterioration of the racial stock.

This would most likely account for the fact that most of the living creatures of the present are represented in the fossil record by larger, more highly developed members of the same species. It might likewise partially account for the extinction of so many once highly developed forms of living creatures that once inhabited the earth, but are now known only as fossils. Furthermore, it would explain the phenomenon of the atrophy of once-valuable organs until they become vestigial, or even disappear.

Thus it seems evident that if evolution has taken place on any large scale at all (that is, of course, progressive evolution), it must have done so at complete variance with the indications of all modern genetic research and indeed with all basic physical law. Most of the proffered evidence for evolution can be better interpreted in the light of the law of deterioration, and with far better scientific basis.

3

MODERN SCIENCE AND THE FLOOD

IN THE BOOK OF GENESIS, beginning at chapter 6, is the record of the greatest physical catastrophe the earth has ever experienced, the global deluge of the days of Noah. All men, as well as all land animals, except those whom God chose to save in the ark, were destroyed by a great world-enveloping flood that was sent as divine punishment because "all flesh had corrupted his way upon the earth."

The biblical record of the deluge clearly refers to a great flood which completely inundated the entire globe. Some writers, because of supposed geological and archaeological difficulties, have maintained that the flood was only a basin overflow, applicable only to the known world of that period at most. Most critics of the Bible have, in fact, dismissed the entire tale as purely legendary.

However, if the Bible is allowed to speak for itself, an unprejudiced reader would surely understand the writer of the account to be referring to a worldwide deluge. For example, the following passages can be sensibly understood in no other way: "I do bring a flood of waters upon the earth, to destroy all flesh, wherein is the breath of life, from under heaven; and every thing that is in the earth shall die" (Gen. 6:17).

"Every living substance that I have made will I destroy from off the face of the earth" (Gen. 7:4).

"And the waters prevailed exceedingly upon the earth; and all the high hills, that were under the whole heaven, were covered. Fifteen cubits upward did the waters prevail; and the mountains were covered" (Gen. 7:19-20).

"And every living substance was destroyed which was upon the face of the ground, both man, and cattle, and the creeping things, and the fowl of the heaven; and they were destroyed from the earth: and Noah only remained alive, and they that were with him in the ark" (Gen. 7:23).

"And I will establish my covenant with you; neither shall all flesh be cut off any more by the waters of a flood; neither shall there any more be a flood to destroy the earth" (Gen. 9:11).

One of two such passages might be passed off as figurative or as examples of Hebrew literary exaggeration, but when the same theme of universal inundation and destruction is emphasized again and again in the verses quoted and in numerous others, then it seems quite out of reason to attempt to impress any other meaning upon the account than the writer was obviously intending to convey to his readers, which evidently was that of a worldwide catastrophic diluvial judgment.

In fact, it is quite likely that with conditions of longevity prevailing as described in the Bible, the earth's population would have so increased by this time (more than 1,600 years after the creation of Adam, if one follows the Ussher chronology) that a large part of the earth would almost certainly have been populated, necessitating a worldwide flood if all mankind were to be destroyed thereby.

Furthermore, if all the mountains even in the immediate vicinity, patently including the mountains of Ararat on which the ark eventually grounded—one peak of which is over three miles above sea level—were submerged, it would quite obviously be impossible for the flood *not* to have also attained the same

elevation in other regions, since the record states that
such conditions prevailed for 150 days at least.

But even more important, the entire story is filled
with manifest absurdities if the flood described were
only a localized event. The elaborate provisions for
the preservation of life in the ark were utterly unneces-
sary and unwarranted. God could merely have warned
Noah to move into a region where the flood would not
come, which he could have done with far less time
and labor than was needed in .constructing and out-
fitting the ark. The same is true for the animals, which
the record says God caused to come to the ark; the
birds especially might easily have flown to dry land.
Finally, God's promise that there would never again be
such a destructive flood upon the earth (Gen. 9:11)
would have been proved false, because there have
been many floods since which were at least as great as
that envisioned by the proponents of the local flood
theory.

The biblical record implies that the cause and
character of the flood was both tidal and atmospheric.
Such a gigantic catastrophe must have profoundly
changed the geographic and stratigraphic features of
the earth's surface as it then was, making it impossible
now to discern geologically with any degree of assurance those things that took place in the ages before
the flood. Thus, if actually there was a worldwide
aqueous calamity of the sort described in the Bible,
the fossil record becomes meaningless, as far as prov-
ing evolution is concerned. And, as we have seen,
world history as interpreted from fossils is the only
evidence of any value remaining for the theory of
evolution.

Consequently, in spite of overwhelming ethnological,
philological, archaeological and geological evidence
that there actually was a universal deluge, evolutionary

scientists dogmatically maintain that the flood story of the Bible is purely legendary.

The credo which has been held by most geologists for over a hundred years is called uniformitarianism. This doctrine "assumes the assumption" that all natural, observable phenomena, in both the living and the nonliving realms, can be explained as to origin and development in terms of purely natural laws and processes. As applied to geology, it means that all the mountains, the rivers, the huge stratigraphic deposits, in short, all features of the earth's surface, are explainable as the result of the slow processes of sedimentation, erosion, contraction, radioactivity, and other actions of natural forces, all working over almost infinitely long periods of time. This theory is based not so much on objective proof as on a process of rationalization, it being assumed unscientific to invoke unnatural events such as creation or the flood to explain phenomena that now seem to conform to natural laws.

The popularity of uniformitarianism dates from its enunciation by Sir Charles Lyell a good many years before the appearance of Darwin's work, which was profoundly influenced by that of Lyell. However, the idea was not at all new; its origin is hidden in the obscurity of antiquity and has always found expression in some form or other. With the renewed interest in both science and Christianity that came with the Renaissance period, nevertheless the dominant theory of geology became the flood theory and remained so until the time of Lyell and Darwin. A great many brilliant investigators held this view, which was based not on a philosophy or even on faith, but on thousands of observed facts in the field. It is true that some of these men developed bizarre explanations for some of the data, but the commonsense logic of much of their writings is still irrefutable.

The geologic time scale, which we have mentioned

previously and which is the backbone of the uniformitarian view of geology, was worked out long ago, chiefly from the observed order of the fossils in a small corner of western Europe and in New York State. There are assumed to be four great eras:

1. The Primary, which is often classed as two eras, the Archaeozoic and the Proterozoic, is supposed to represent the ages before life appeared to any extent on the earth. It is denoted by those rocks which contain few or no fossils and are thus supposed to be the oldest rocks of all.

2. The Paleozoic Era is marked by rocks containing fossils of the lower forms of life, especially invertebrates, fishes, insects and amphibians. It is subdivided into several large systems according to the forms of life found in the various rocks. These systems are, beginning with the oldest, the Cambrian, the Ordovician, the Silurian, the Devonian, the Carboniferous (now commonly replaced by two systems, the Mississippian and the Pennsylvanian), and the Permian. Of course, each system is further subdivided.

3. The Mesozoic Era is supposed to be the age of reptiles and is divided into three main systems, the Triassic, the Jurassic and the Cretaceous. The Cenozoic Era is the last of the geologic eras and is divided into two main systems. The first of these is called the Tertiary and is also known as the age of mammals. There are five series in this system known, in ascending order, as the Paleocene, the Eocene, the Oligocene, the Miocene, and the Pliocene.

4. The other system is usually called the Quaternary and includes the Pleistocene Series, in which man is supposed to have appeared (although many paleontologists now claim that man must have appeared well back into the Tertiary because of the many finds of skeletons and artifacts of true humans in possible

Tertiary deposits). The Quaternary also includes the Recent, often called the age of man.

It is usually to be inferred from most textbooks that this order—not only of the geologic eras but also of the systems and series and even formations—is observed all over the world in the same inviolable order. This idea, in a different form, was first developed by Professor Werner, a German who taught that the stratigraphic deposits always occurred in the same vertical order according to their mineral or lithologic character—granites, limestones, schists, sandstones, etc. This theory was called the "onion-coat" theory and was very widely held by materialistic geologists for a long time. It has now given way to a theory of biological onion-coats, in which the order of the fossils is thought to be always the same. The mineral or lithologic nature of the rocks is now considered incidental, the age and chronological position of any given formation depending determinately upon the contained fossils.

The circle of reasoning involved here should be immediately evident. The fact of evolution is necessarily assumed in building up the geological series; rocks containing simpler fossils are called old, and rocks containing more complex and specialized forms are considered young. Then the paleontological series thus constructed is taken as proof of the fact of evolution.

This method of identifying the rocks cannot be overemphasized. The physical characteristics and even the stratigraphical position are given only very minor consideration when their age is being decided. This matter depends almost entirely upon the contained fossils and is usually settled by laboratory workers who may never have seen the actual deposits.

However, in spite of the apparent dangers involved in such procedures, this system of classification seems to have worked out fairly satisfactorily at least in North

America and Europe, although there still remains considerable doubt as to ultimate correlation with the geology of other parts of the world. It seems that, in general, the time order of deposition of the strata is represented fairly well by the geologic time classification as given. The really essential point of difference between the commonly accepted geology and flood geology is not the *relative time* of deposition of different rock strata, but the actual *total time* elapsed while they were being deposited. First, however, it is well to point out that the accepted stratigraphic order and system is far from inviolable and involves many hard-to-explain exceptions and anomalies.

In the first place, the total depth of all fossiliferous strata is supposed to be about a hundred miles. However, the greatest depth ever actually observed is about two or three miles. In any one exposure, two or three systems or even fewer are all that are usually represented. At no place in the world, as far as ever observed, is the complete or even partially complete geological column exposed or even known to exist. It has been built up entirely by superposition of deposits from all over the world.

Furthermore, many different formations, widely separated in geologic time, have been found resting directly upon the primitive rocks. Many cases have been observed here in America of the very youngest Quaternary rocks resting directly upon the Primary with all the intervening ages omitted. The same thing can probably be said for every rock system of importance. In fact, frequently the oldest rocks (i.e., non-fossil-bearing) may be on the surface and have the physical appearance of young rocks, soft and unconsolidated. Young rocks, on the other hand, may well be as crystalline and metamorphic as the very oldest, and frequently are.

It is also generally accepted in geology that any

fossiliferous formation may lie directly upon any other formation in the whole of the series below it, and that it is not at all to be expected that a given formation need lie directly upon the formation that immediately precedes it in geologic age. When intervening formations are missing, it is assumed that the missing periods can be accounted for as periods of erosion rather than deposition. Often, however, such missing periods are not at all obvious physically, and are only inferred from fossil evidence. They are called disconformities or diastems when the beds on both sides seem to have been normally deposited without intervening deformation. Quite often the two sets of beds are parallel and give every indication of having been deposited successively without any great period of time or erosion between. The disconformities are, in such cases, discernible only on the basis of the contained fossils. If it were not for the preconceived opinions as to the evolutionary sequence of the fossils, there would be no reason for saying that such beds could not have been deposited with no great lapse of time between. This sort of thing is not an isolated pheonomenon, but one of which many examples could be cited.

Even more surprisingly, many examples are now known to geologists of strata occurring in the wrong order and, furthermore, in perfect conformity. That is, great areas containing "old" fossils are found to rest perfectly naturally upon rocks containing "young" fossils. Sometimes such inversions have obviously been produced by normal faulting and folding, of which the rocks of the earth's crust give much evidence. Often, however, there is no physical indication at all that the beds came to be in their existing positions by any other means than normal deposition. This cannot be allowed, however, because it would immediately prove that the "young" fossils are older than the "old" ones, at least in time of deposition, and this would obviously necessitate sacrificing the notion of organic evolution.

To avoid such action, we have the remarkable theory of the horizontal thrust fault, according to which great masses of rock were severed from their original formations and somehow lifted up and shoved over on top of the adjacent areas, following which, surface erosion through the immediate subsequent ages removed the upper deposits, finally leaving only the older rocks lying on the younger ones beneath!

If such things as this have ever happened upon the planet, they must have been caused by forces of far greater intensity than anything ever observed by humankind in the present age. There is most certainly no experimental or observational basis for such an explanation, a fact which is most inconsistent with the rather vaunted geologic dogma of uniformity. In fact, no less an authority than William Bowie, long-time director of the United States Coast and Geodetic Survey, and one of the world's greatest authorities on isostasy and tectonics, considered such horizontal faulting "absurd, from an engineering point of view."

Nevertheless, scores of examples of this phenomenon exist. Every large mountain range in the world that has been adequately examined (and mountainous regions are those that *have* been most thoroughly examined geologically) has been found to contain large areas of these upside-down strata. A vast area in Montana and Alberta, including all of the Glacier National Park, has fossils of the Paleozoic Era or earlier overlying dinosaur bones and other fossils of the Cretaceous. This region is the divide between not only the Atlantic and Pacific oceans, but also between Hudson Bay and the Gulf of Mexico. Thus, the highest region of North America consists of a stratum of Pre-Cambrian limestone resting perfectly naturally on a Cretaceous bed. In Tennessee and Georgia, a great "fault" continuing for hundreds of miles consists of Cambrian deposits resting quite normally on Carboniferous. The great Bannock Overthrust of Utah and the Heart Mountain Thrust of Wyoming, along with many other examples in the Rockies, offer more illustrations of huge areas of rocks, thousands of feet thick, that must have been shoved up and over the adjacent areas, without leaving any evidence at the so-called fault line or elsewhere of their incredible journeys. Much of the Swiss Alpine region is in this upside-down condition. The same is true of the Scottish Highlands and the mountains of India. One of these displacements in northern China has been followed for more than 500 miles. A similar area of some 85,000 square miles is known in Scandinavia. Every part of the world yields other examples.

However, even if the geologic time scale is assumed to be substantially correct as far as the relative positions of the various strata are concerned, the flood theory can account for their deposition thus equally as satisfactorily as the theory of great ages, and probably more so.

The predeluge world, like the present world, was undoubtedly one in which lived a great variety of different kinds of creatures. Then, as now, they did not all live together or in the same type of environment, but each particular kind would live in the environment for which he was fitted.

Therefore, a great catastrophe of the kind described in the Bible would not be expected to pile all types of creatures together heterogeneously throughout the world. Rather, it would necessarily destroy together the particular assemblages of creatures living in the same environment. The currents would transport such assemblages together, and finally bury them together. This, of course, would not be expected to be an inviolable rule but would generally hold true. Thus,

two or more strata might be deposited quite simultaneously, but contain completely different groups of
future fossils because of their different sources, directions of transport and final deposition localities.

On the other hand, evolutionary geology teaches, by
implication at least, that only one assemblage of organisms was living at any one time in the history of the
world and that, therefore, these organisms can be used
to identify any rock strata formed during that age.
There can be no basis for this assumption other than
evolutionary presuppositions, because such is certainly
not the case in the modern world, which is supposed
to be "the key to the past."

The biblical deluge was both terrestrial and atmospheric in nature. Tremendous volumes of water poured
from the heavens for forty days and nights. At the
same time, "the fountains of the great deep were
broken up," most likely implying great subterranean
and subaqueous disturbances, which would have created
great tidal waves and ejected great amounts of juvenile
water. The great complex of hydrodynamic currents
and forces thus generated would then undertake its
divinely ordained mission of destruction and purifica-
tion of the antediluvian world.

Such a flood would necessarily tend to affect first
and bury lowest the creatures inhabiting the deep
ocean, then those in shallower waters. Then the waters
and disturbed sediments would overtake the amphib-
ious and land-bordering creatures. Above these would
be buried swamp, marsh, and low river-flat creatures,
including especially reptiles. Higher mammals would
usually be able to retreat from the rising waters to
some extent, but also would be eventually drowned
and perhaps buried in the sediments. Finally man, the
chief object of the waters, would be overtaken and
carried under. There were also probably many inland
seas and waterways at various elevations. Burial of

the creatures in these inland basins would account for the present existence of marine strata in some of the higher beds. Thus the flood would in general have tended to form just such strata, and in just the order as the geologic age scale purports to represent. These strata would perhaps in many instances be reworked and redeposited in the later periods of the retreating floodwaters, and perhaps also in the succeeding centuries. Also, in their semiplastic state during and soon after the flood, they would have been subject to much distortion of all kinds, caused by great forces generated by the hydrostatic and hydrodynamic pressures of the deluge waters, and by the redisposition of the prediluvian topography. This might partially account for the existence of the great faults and folds in the sedimentary rocks of the crust.

Another factor tending to cause the deposition of the strata in the order in which they are found would be the sorting action of moving water, which would tend to separate particles, whether organic or inorganic, into assemblages of similar sizes and shapes. Also, the rapidity of settling and deposition of particular fossils would be at least partially controlled by their specific gravity. The usually more dense marine organisms would therefore tend to settle first, then amphibia, mammals, etc.

This of course is but the barest outline of the probable geologic activity of the deluge. Further geologic work would be accomplished on the surface as the lands were uplifted in places and the waters retreated. Abnormal geologic and meteorologic conditions perhaps prevailed for centuries before the present condition of approximate equilibrium in the earth's crust and atmosphere was attained.

The deluge theory, then, seems to offer an acceptable framework within which to explain all the multitudinous data with which geology deals. The main criticism of the theory has always been on the basis of the time element involved. It has been maintained, by those few geologists who have adequately considered it and then rejected it, that the immense sedimentary rock beds of the earth and their fossils cannot possibly be attributed only to one great cataclysm, but that their formation must have occupied aeons of time. This assertion cannot be proved, however, in the very nature of the case. It is based on the assumption of uniformitarianism which, however reasonable such an assumption may be normally, obviously cannot have held valid during the time of the deluge if the deluge actually occurred.

Obviously, in a book of this size it is impossible to give a complete discussion of all phases of geology, and their harmonization with the flood theory, and to explain all phenomena and formations which may at first seem to be inexplicable on this basis. However, in the book *The Genesis Flood,* coauthored by the writer (see Bibliography), a comprehensive and documented treatment of the more important problems in flood geology and related subjects can be found.

Actually, the flood theory of geology is only slightly less uniformitarian in character, if any, than orthodox geology. The catchword of the uniformitarian view of geology is that "the present is the key to the past." However, one does not go very far in the study of historical geology, as now interpreted, before he sees that "uniformitarianism" is actually a rather gross misnomer. Present geologic processes, such as erosion, sedimentation, volcanism, diastrophism, glaciation, etc., are supposed to be able to account for all stratigraphic and physiographic phenomena. However, if the present character of the activity of these agencies is to be taken as typical, it is obvious that they cannot begin to do any such thing.

In recent years, in fact, many geologists have recognized the limitations of a consistent uniformitarianism, such as had been advocated by practically all geologists since the time of Lyell. They have come to recognize the necessity of a rather large extrapolation from present geologic processes in order to make a reasonable accounting for the existence of many of the earth's geologic phenomena.

For example, when in recorded history has there ever been a great outpouring of volcanic lava such as must have formed the terrain extending over great areas of the Pacific Northwest and in many other parts of the world? Where has there ever been observed a mountain uplifted thousands of feet against the huge forces of gravity and friction? What about the great rock ruptures that are supposed to have formed the Great Rift of Africa, the formation of the great fault scarp on the eastern edge of the Sierra Nevadas, or the one that formed Grand Teton, or thousands of others almost as spectacular? Speculative geologic history is replete with the erosion of vast peneplains, but where is such to be found in the modern world? Wherein lies the present-day observational basis to account, on the basis of uniformity, for the great ice sheets, thousands of feet thick, that are supposed to have covered most of Europe and North America many times in past ages? What about the coal beds, which are said to have been formed over long ages as the result of alternate submergences and emergences of peat bogs, the cycle repeated scores of times on the same spot (and this in spite of the fact that many fossil tree trunks have been found extending through several coal seams, each presumably formed during one such cycle)? Who has actually observed great canyons excavated through solid rock to depths of thousands of feet, or the deposition of great silt deposits over great areas and hundreds of feet deep by periglacial winds, or the formation of great alluvial plains hundreds of square miles in area and hundreds of feet deep by any modern river? Such events as these, and many more with which historical geology deals, most definitely cannot be adequately described or explained in terms of their modern counterparts.

Even the customary appeal to great ages of time cannot be made in many such instances. Modern volcanoes could never produce the volcanic terrains of many parts of the world, not to mention the tremendous igneous intrusions that have formed the great dikes and sills, the great batholiths, etc., the like of which has never been observed by man in the process of formation. The slight earth movements of the present day, even those accompanying great earthquakes, can by no type of legitimate extrapolation, be held to be incipient movements of the gigantic magnitude and intricate complexity that have been experienced by the earth at some time or times in the past. The erosion of deep gorges through solid rock by normal river flows, no less than the erosion of vast peneplains near sea level by ordinary stream action, are things which not only have no observational basis, but which seem to be precluded by basic principles of stream mechanics.

All such events can only be explained by admitting that present-day phenomena are *not* adequate to account for them. The flood theory also recognizes this, but postulates only one great physical revolution, chiefly diluvial in character, but also and necessarily accompanied by great volcanic and telluric movements, far eclipsing anything ever experienced by the earth before or since, and perhaps also followed by glaciation of tremendous extent.

The so-called uniformity theory professedly ridicules the idea of geologic catastrophe, while actually having to resort to a great number of geological events and phenomena of character and intensity quite outside the scope of anything ever observed in the present age.

Since this is the case, it follows that the flood theory is quite as consistent with a true scheme of uniformitarianism as is the theory that has appropriated the name, and in many ways much more so. The flood theory furthermore has good basis in written and orally transmitted records, whereas the presently accepted interpretation of historical geology necessarily has no such basis at all.

There is surely no intention here to impugn either the abilities or the motives of modern geologists. Most of them are capable, sincere men, diligently, sacrificially and honestly devoted to the study of science for its own sake. The writer has taken considerable graduate work in geology and has known and studied under some outstanding men in this field. Generally speaking, their adoption of the uniformity theory has not been because of an antireligious bias, but because they believed it to be the most scientific approach to geologic study. However, it seems very likely that the effect of their training in the uniformitarian tradition, together with the long-time preponderance of geological opinion, has kept them from ever even considering the possible merits of the diluvial theory.

Most of the results of the past hundred years of geologic study and research would be valid regardless of which theory is correct. None of the great mass of useful geologic data or techniques would have to be discarded if the flood theory were accepted. Only the time element and the evolutionary implications would be sacrificed, and neither of these has any genuine value in geologic research. As far as the evolutionary deductions are concerned, we have already examined somewhat the very dubious character of the entire philosophy of progressive evolution. The fact that the only real evidence left favoring evolution is the evidence from geology, and that all other evidence of biological change is much better evidence of deterioration, would — by strong implication — make the evolutionary framework of geology exceedingly questionable. The other major item to be revised by geology is the matter of time involved in the formation of the strata. This also will be found to be a very questionable element in the theory, as usually held by orthodox geology. Methods of measuring geologic time and their dependability are briefly discussed later in the chapter.

There are also in geology certain very positive evidences for the flood which we should mention. The outstanding of these, probably, are the enormous graveyards of fossils that are found all over the world. Almost without exception, the indications are, from the appearance and manner of preservation of the fossils, that they were buried suddenly; but nothing of the sort is taking place now. It is known that such few fishes as die natural deaths are usually soon devoured in whole or partially by other creatures. In any event, they do not settle into the ocean or riverbed but float on the surface until eaten or decomposed. A modern fish buried whole in sediment normally deposited would be a unique specimen. When land animals die, their remains are almost always quickly decomposed. This is well substantiated by the fact that it is practically impossible to find bones of modern animals in the process of fossilization.

Then how can the ancient fossil deposits be accounted for on the basis of uniformity? The extent and wealth of these deposits is one of the marvels of geology. This fact is so well known that it hardly needs elaboration. Fossil fish beds have been found which extend miles in every direction and contain fish buried in whole shoals by the millions. The fish have every appearance of having been buried alive and with great suddenness. The same is true of the reptilian deposits of the Rockies and the Black Hills and many other parts of the world. The amazing elephant beds of Siberia, the hippopotamus beds of Sicily, the horse beds of France and other parts of Europe, to say nothing of the shells of marine organisms, which probably form the greater part of the stratified deposits of the globe, all point to a great, worldwide catastrophe in which "the world that then was, being overflowed with water, perished." In no other way can the sudden extinction of the dinosaurs and the great mammals of the past be accounted for. They were certainly not eliminated by the much less hardy creatures of the present order in the struggle for existence.

The Siberian deposits of elephants, or mammoths, should be mentioned further. Literally millions of these animals have been entombed in the vast wildernesses of that land. Some explorers have said that on some of the northern islands particularly, the ground consisted almost entirely of mammoth bones. A regular trade in fossil ivory has afforded livelihood to the natives of this region since at least 900 A.D. In the more northern parts of the country, where the ground is perpetually frozen, some remains of these beasts have been preserved whole, with even the skin and hair intact. From the evidence of the congested blood in the blood vessels of the elephants so preserved, scientists say they must have died by drowning, in spite of the fact that the modern elephant is a very strong and long swimmer. The remains of the last meal, consisting of elephant grass and other plants now utterly foreign to the region, have been found in their stomachs. What is true of the mammoths is also true to a lesser extent of many other animals whose fossil remains have been marvelously preserved in Siberia. This is especially true of the rhinoceros, who is now as much a stranger to Siberia as the elephant. These animals were very evidently then living in a land where the climate was mild and afforded an abundance of vegetation. This was absolutely necessary to support such hordes of the animals as lived there. But there is no sign of such climate or vegetation now. That they were suddenly buried by a great deluge, which was accompanied by an almost instantaneous and a very extreme change of climate, is equally evident. No slowly encroaching glacial age or any other tenet of evolutionary geology can account for these amazing finds.

The Siberian mummies are an especially vivid illustration of one outstanding fact that paleontology unquestionably reveals; that is, that at one time in the history of the globe there was a worldwide temperate climate. The remains of coral reefs formed by sea creatures that can live only in warm waters have been found so far north that it is believed now that they underlie the very poles themselves. Tropical animals have been found in large numbers as fossils not only in Siberia but in Greenland, Alaska, and practically every region in the world. Fossil ferns and other tropical and temperate vegetation have likewise been found in large numbers in the polar regions. Even in the very coldest region of the globe, the great continent of Antarctica, extensive coal beds have been found, extending almost to the South Pole itself.

Geologists also believe there have been one or more periods of earth history when large areas of the globe were submerged by great ice sheets. There is sound basis for suggesting that the supposed evidences for these ice ages could be better interpreted in terms of water action, especially the earlier ones. The glacial till from the last ice sheet, however, is of a different type from the others and probably does indicate true glacial conditions. The cause of this ice age or ages, however, as well as the cause of the worldwide temperate climate or climates preceding them, has never yet been determined, and constitutes one of the most perplexing unsolved problems of geology. The principle of uniformity seems completely incapable of supplying the answer. A worldwide temperate climate preceding the deluge, however, with the latter possibly followed by extensive glaciation, fits well into the framework of flood geology.

Another geologic evidence for the flood is the existence of raised beaches and terraces, indicating former high water levels. These raised beaches and terraces are found all over the world, often hundreds and even thousands of feet above present water levels. They are found along coastlines, on the sides of river valleys, and along the shores of great inland basins, in truly worldwide distribution. There are a number of ways in which geologists have suggested these terraces might be formed, most of which have very definite objections. By far the most logical explanation for most of them at least is that they were formed by the waters of the flood, possibly over many years, as the lands were uplifted and the waters receded. Rivers carried much greater discharges and the oceans were at a much higher level relative to the land than now. Lakes and inland basins formerly contained much more water and submerged far greater areas than at present. These facts surely can be understood far better in terms of postdeluge conditions than in any other way.

Finally, the very fact that most of the sedimentary rocks of the earth were obviously laid down under moving water, including the peaks of most of the great mountain ranges, is itself a strong indication of the flood, although it has actually been made the basis of evolutionary geology.

The physical cause and character of the deluge must necessarily be somewhat a matter of speculation. There are, however, some very interesting possibilities suggested by the Genesis account of creation and the flood, which we shall now examine.

It is intimated in Genesis 2 that there was no rain-fall, such as we know it now, in the antediluvian period. Also the rainbow is later mentioned specifically as a divine token given to Noah by God after the flood, implying that atmospheric water, if any, was always in the vapor state and could not form a rainbow. The statement in Genesis 1 that the "waters which were above the firmament" were separated during the creation from the "waters which were below the firmament" would imply that at this time there was a great body of water vapor surrounding the earth above its atmosphere. The word translated "firmament" literally means "expanse" and would seem to be descriptive of the atmosphere, or at least the troposphere (which is that part of the atmosphere in which there are now convection currents, storms, clouds, etc.—below the stratosphere). Certain very unusual atmospheric and climatic conditions are also indicated by the extreme longevity of the antediluvians.

Such a condition is also strongly implied by the biblical record of a tremendous rain, continuing for forty days and forty nights, as one of the causes of the deluge. We have already shown that the Bible teaches very clearly and emphatically that the deluge was worldwide, and therefore must have required a worldwide cause. A mere local rainstorm, however severe, could never have produced the biblical flood. It is certain that present atmospheric and meteorologic conditions could never be such as to produce a universal rainstorm lasting for forty days. There is only enough water vapor in the atmosphere at present to cover the lands to a depth of a few inches.

However, there is enough water in the oceans of the world to cover the entire earth to a depth of about two miles, if the terrestrial topography were smoothed to a common elevation. It is conceivable that much of the present oceanic water was, before the deluge, stored in

a great vapor canopy surrounding the earth. It may
have extended throughout the present stratosphere and
ionosphere (the ionosphere is at present a vast layer
above the stratosphere in which there are great numbers of atoms and molecules in an ionized state, and
in which are produced many remarkable electrical
phenomena), or may even have been largely outside
the present bounds of these layers. It is even conceivable that much of this water vapor could have
existed in the form of dissociated oxygen and hydrogen.

There is not much known as yet about the upper
atmosphere, even as it exists at present, and it is surely
possible that vastly different conditions may have prevailed in the past, as seems to be implied in the Bible
record. In some way, the great canopy condensed and
descended upon the earth, then, at the time of the
deluge.

There is no intimation in Scripture as to what may
have triggered the precipitation of the canopy, and
neither is there any way by which it could be ascer-
tained scientifically. One could speculate as to possible
physical mechanisms—passage of the earth through a
cometary train or a swarm of meteorites, widespread
volcanic eruptions, a shift in the earth's axis, etc. But
such speculations would only be that and nothing else.
It is not unreasonable to suggest that the direct intervention of God Himself may have been involved, because of His intense personal concern (note Gen.
6:17). If He did use secondary mechanisms, He has
not been pleased to reveal them in the biblical record.

This great canopy of vapor, if it existed, would have
resulted in just such physical phenomena as are indicated in Scripture and geology to have prevailed before
the flood. It would probably have been invisible to the
inhabitants of the earth, but would have intercepted
and filtered out much of the short wave-length radiation that now reaches the earth, including ultraviolet

and X rays, and the mysterious and intensely powerful cosmic rays. In fact, the earth's present blanket of invisible water vapor throughout the atmosphere makes life possible on the earth by this very action. If the ultraviolet and cosmic radiation were not thus filtered before reaching the earth, it would quickly destroy all life if it could reach the earth in full strength.

Therefore, the existence of the prediluvian "waters above the firmament" would have caused a healthier physical environment than now exists on the surface of the earth. This would be further enhanced by the fact that the canopy would have the effect of preventing extremes of heat and cold, resulting in a uniformly warm, probably subtropical, climate all over the globe. This phenomenon has already been mentioned as demonstrated geologically by the discovery in polar regions of many evidences of former warm climatic conditions there. This uniform climate, together with a probably much different and more gentle arrangement of topography than has existed since the flood, would have caused much different meteorological conditions. High winds, storms, etc., would have been impossible, since they result basically from temperature differences. Indeed, it is unlikely that even rain as we know it now could have been produced, though there would have been a continuous interchange of water near the surface, from evaporation and transpiration into the air, then back to the land at night as dew and mist. This inference is also supported by the phenomenon mentioned in Genesis 2:5-6: ". . . for the Lord God had not caused it to rain upon the earth . . . . But there went up a mist from the earth, and watered the whole face of the ground." Also, with no water except transparent water vapor in the air, the rainbow would be unknown until after the flood, when its first appearance made it a beautiful and striking token of God's promise to Noah.

There may also have been great underground reservoirs of water under pressure, implied in the term "waters below the firmament," and in the later reference to the "fountains of the great deep." These would have surface or underground outlets at certain places and thus maintain rivers and a subsurface water table which would support luxuriant vegetation everywhere.

It should be emphasized that these suggestions are merely suggestions; they are not specifically taught in Scripture. However, available meteorologic and geologic knowledge, together with the various biblical statements concerning antediluvian phenomena, all show striking harmony with the outlined theory, or some modification of it.

As we have seen in the preceding chapter, modern genetic research has well demonstrated that hereditary variation in living things is caused chiefly by gene mutations. The same research has also demonstrated that these changes are nearly always deteriorations and that the occurrence of such mutations follows statistical laws. They seem to be caused by some disorganizing medium, especially short wave-length radiation, entering the chromosomes of the germ cells. The rate of mutation in a species, therefore, depends on the rate at which such rays will penetrate the germ cells, which in turn is statistically dependent on the amount of radiation entering the environment.

The antediluvian environment, as pictured above, would have far less such radiation than does the present one. Therefore, there must have been fewer mutations. Everything favored the continued productions of larger, stronger, longer-lived specimens of every type of creature. This, of course, is what we have already seen the fossil record to indicate. According to the Bible, many men lived to be more than nine hundred years old. However, with the vapor canopy precipitated at the time of the deluge, the mutation

rate speeded up, the size and strength of the average
creature deteriorated, many species became extinct,
and the length of the life-span began a steady decline.
These trends are still apparent today, although modern
medical and sanitary science has, to a considerable
extent, masked the natural trend as far as man is concerned.

This theory clarifies and makes more vivid the pic-
turesque language of Genesis that "the windows [liter-
ally, floodgates] of heaven were opened." At the same
time, "the fountains of the great deep were broken up,"
implying a tremendous tidal upheaval of the "waters
that were under the firmament."

It is now easier to realize something of the overwhelming nature of this catastrophe. Certainly every
foot of the earth's surface must have been profoundly
disturbed and altered. All creatures, except those at
home in the water and those preserved by God in the
ark, must have violently perished, many of them being
buried alive in the whirling sediments and debris.
When, a year later, Noah and his family came out of
the ark, they saw a tremendously different world. No
canopy of vapor filtered and diffused the sun's rays
any longer and a rainbow appeared in the sky as a
sign from God that this aqueous judgment would
never again be visited on the earth (and, indeed, it
could not if the upper waters were no longer there).

It is manifest that this great event, if it occurred,
would be preserved not only in the rocks, but in the
history and traditions of the race. That this is actually
the case is known to every student of ethnology. Practically every country and tribe in the world has its
own flood story, many of them amazingly similar to
the Bible story, even in details such as the sending
of the dove and the raven to search for land and the
offering of sacrifices to the deity when the waters
subsided. Yet the similarity is not so marked as to

permit the idea that somehow the Genesis account had penetrated to all these scattered peoples. All of the stories, save that in Genesis, have been distorted with all sorts of impossible and absurd fancies. Yet, they all obviously have arisen from the same original source. Since most of them were handed down by word of mouth, this is exactly what would be expected. To cite only a few examples, in order to illustrate the worldwide nature of this tradition, flood stories have been found in such widely scattered lands as China, Babylon, Wales, Russia, India, America (practically all Indian tribes), Hawaii, Scandinavia, Sumatra, Peru, Polynesia, and in fact, every region in the world save certain parts of Africa. Geologists who dogmatically affirm that the universal flood is purely legendary seem to completely ignore this powerful ethnological evidence.

The very peoples and population of the world are a convincing testimony to their origin from a common stock at about the time and place indicated in the biblical record. Archaeological evidence invariably points to some point near the eastern shore of the Mediterranean as the cradle of civilization. The recorded or otherwise trustworthy history of nations elsewhere in the world always indicates either a migration from this area or else fades into oblivion at a time when Chaldea and other eastern nations are known to have been in an advanced stage of civilization.

Furthermore, assuming that the present human race sprang originally from two people, whether they were the original apelike Dawn Man and his mate, or Noah and his wife, we find that the present population of the world supports the latter view and makes the former seem ridiculous. The population of the world in 1800 has been estimated at about 850 million. It is now about three billion. We can say that the population has doubled in about the past hundred years.

There is no objective reason to suppose that this rate of one hundred years for the population of the world to double itself should have been greatly different at other periods in the history of the world. In 1650, the world population was only about 400 million. The present rate implies a considerably more rapid increase. Now, if the original population was two, we can find by logarithms that the population would have to have doubled itself exactly thirty times to produce the present number of people in the world.

If the original pair lived, for example, 500,000 years ago, which is considerably less than the average evolutionary estimate, the average interval for doubling of the population would have been 16,667 years, which is absurd. If, on the other hand, all people are descended from Noah and his wife, who according to some biblical chronologists must have lived about 4,500 years ago, then the average interval for doubling is 150 years, which is entirely reasonable.

One other phase of the flood story has often been questioned. It is said that Noah's ark could not possibly have held two members of all the animal species in the world. However, it should be remembered that it was only necessary for Noah to provide for two members of each "kind" (with seven each of the clean animals for sacrifice). As mentioned previously, the term "kind" is probably much more elastic than our modern "species" concept, and it is sure that there was not an excessive number of original "kinds." (Adam was able to give names to all of them in less than one day, according to Gen. 2:20.) Only the land animals were taken into the ark, of course, and there are comparatively few kinds of land animals which are large. Most of the mammals, birds and reptiles could have been placed in cages and stacked in tiers. The dimensions of the ark are given in terms of the cubit, which probably at that time was about eighteen inches in length. If so, then it can be quickly calculated that the ark had a capacity of some one and a half million cubic feet, easily equivalent to that of over five hundred of our modern railroad cattle cars. Its dimensions were ideal for both storage purposes and for stability in the turbulent waters of the flood. The geographical distribution of animals was possibly quite different before the flood, but in any event Noah did not have to find and bring the animals to the ark; the Bible says that God caused them to come to him, possibly through some intuition of the approaching catastrophe. Thus there is nothing impossible or unreasonable about the biblical account of the ark and its inhabitants.

The question of the age of the earth must be considered briefly before concluding this chapter. A literal reading of the biblical record will yield an age of only several thousand years for the earth. On the other hand, geologists usually estimate the earth to be several billion years old. This matter of geological dating is very important, both in estimating the earth's age and in fixing the absolute depositional date of the various formations. However, it is a very detailed and involved subject and one that cannot be adequately handled here in such a brief compass.

The chronometers most often used in the past have been the rate of cooling of the earth, the deposits of sediment at the mouths of rivers as compared with the sedimentary deposits of the earth's surface, rates of erosion of the earth's surface, the amount of salt and other chemicals in the ocean, and radioactivity. Scientists now readily admit that all of these, except possibly the last, are not at all to be trusted and are of practically no value in calculating the earth's age. This admission would most certainly never have been made had not the estimates based on these methods turned out finally to be far too low to permit the present state of the organic world to have been attained by evolution. It is true, however, that the estimate ob-

tained by each of these methods was stretched out of
all justification so that the errors caused by the weak-
nesses inherent in the methods themselves were of
such nature as to give too large an estimate. Nevertheless, the methods were discarded when they proved
unsatisfactory to the theory of evolution. For example,
probably the best and most reliable of all the methods was the one based on the salt in the sea. The
amount of salt in the sea is fairly well known and
also the rate at which the rivers of the world are
emptying more salt into the sea. It was then assumed
that the rate had always been the same and that
originally there was no salt at all in the sea. Upon
these assumptions, which of course were wholly unwarranted and unreasonable, the age of the earth was
estimated as, at the most, one hundred million years.
Since it is extremely probable that the sea contained
a great deal of salt to begin with and also that the
rivers once were much larger than at present and that
the rate of erosion was much more rapid, this estimate
is seen to be enormously too large. However, it has
been discarded by evolutionary geologists as too small.

The only method that has been satisfactory to the
evolutionists is the radioactivity method. It is known
that metals of high atomic weight, such as thorium and
uranium, are constantly being broken down into radium
and eventually into an isotope of lead. The rate of this
decomposition is believed to be constant. Consequently,
when rocks are found containing uranium, thorium or
radium, and lead, the relative amounts of the two
metals in the rocks are taken as an index of their
age. However, there is no dependable way to estimate
how much uranium or thorium may have been leached
out of the sample. This is a common occurrence and,
in fact, most deposits of radioactive minerals have
actually been rejected for age determinations because
of the belief that this had taken place. Neither is
there any way of knowing how much radiogenic lead

may have been originally deposited with the uranium or later introduced in some other way from another source.

In fact, it is quite contrary to the whole tenor of historical geology to say that a deposit of radioactive metal could have remained unaffected by all the effects of telluric movements, igneous activity, ground water flow, chemical action, etc., for hundreds of millions of years or more, to be discovered near the surface in these present days. But if the deposit was affected by any agency during those unimaginably long periods of time, then it is manifestly untrustworthy as a means of measurement. The exact original amounts of metal must be known, and so must the exact amount of material produced by radioactive disintegration during all that time, in order for the age estimate to have any meaning whatever. But it should be very evident that it is not only impossible to *know* that there have *never* been any disturbing factors, but it actually seems quite certain that there *must have been many*.

Furthermore, it should also be obvious that it can never be positively demonstrated that the rate of disintegration has never changed during all those tremendous periods of time. Of course, if the rate has changed, then unless the exact way in which the change has operated is known, it is quite impossible to make any kind of valid age determination. It is known, of course, that the disintegration rate cannot be varied by great extremes of temperature or pressure, or by many other influences that have been brought to bear in the laboratory. Nevertheless, this does not prove that some other influence untried as yet might not change it.

There was evidently a radically different terrestrial environment during the creation period and even during the entire antediluvian period. The tremendous atmospheric and geophysical changes during the year of the flood could very well have affected the rates of all earth processes, including those of radioactive decay. There is still much to be learned of the exact nature and causes of radioactive decay even as it operates in the present.

As a matter of fact, it is known now that some disintegrations can be greatly hastened, and this is the basis of the atomic bomb. Furthermore, there now exists considerable evidence that the natural rate of disintegration may be affected by cosmic radiation, and possibly by still other influences which are not reproduceable in laboratories.

In view of all these and many more difficulties with the radioactivity method that might be enumerated, it is not surprising that results obtained by the method are so erratic. It is quite common to obtain widely divergent results from different samples in the same locality. Out of all the hundreds of age determinations that have been made by this method, there are still less than a dozen from all parts of the world that are considered to be fairly dependable and to fit satisfactorily into the accepted geologic time scale. Most of them have been rejected for one reason or another, quite often simply on the basis that the radioactivity age determination contradicts the geologic time classification already worked out on the basis of the contained fossils.

All things considered, this method of estimating geologic time, no less than its predecessors, has been vastly overrated, and has had built upon it a superstructure of geologic, astronomic and philosophic interpretation which preponderantly overburdens it.

Thus, there is no really scientific proof yet offered that the earth is very old, and a truly objective geology would not suffer on this score either from adopting the deluge hypothesis in place of the so-called uniformitarian framework.

There are a number of natural chronometers which are much more dependable and, as we might expect, give estimates that are much shorter than the ones ordinarily quoted. Some of these are the amount of helium in the atmosphere, the amount of material from meteors that has fallen on the earth, and the amount of juvenile water produced by volcanoes and hot springs, all of which indicate that the earth is extremely youthful as compared with the estimates of the evolutionists.

This discussion might be considerably extended, but it can safely be said in summary that no genuine proof exists that the earth is very old. All methods of geological time measurement in current use are based on the theory of uniformity, ignoring completely the possibility of an original creation and the effects of the Noachian deluge. We are quite justified, scientifically as well as scripturally, in maintaining the traditional position that the earth is not more than several thousand years old.

A remarkable prophecy of our times is given in II Peter 3:3-6, "There shall come in the last days scoffers, walking after their own lusts, and saying, Where is the promise of his coming? For since the fathers fell asleep, all things continue as they were from the beginning of the creation. For this they willingly are ignorant of, that by the word of God the heavens were of old, and the earth standing out of the water and in the water: whereby the world that then was, being overflowed with water, perished."

The modern doctrine of biologic and geologic uniformity is plainly indicated in this prophecy. Note that the doctrine was to teach not only that "all things continue as they were since the *end* of the creation," but rather, "since the *beginning* of the creation," emphasizing that creation itself was to be attributed to natural laws and processes which are still in operation.

This very idea, of course, is the basis of the theory of evolution. Note also that the apparent scientific basis of this uniformitarian principle would have to be based on the willful denial of two great historic facts—the creation and the deluge. During at least these two profoundly important periods of earth history, of course, the uniformity principle could not have been in operation. The creation was accomplished by entirely different means than God now uses in His providential sustaining of the world, which are the only processes that can now be studied. The deluge also marked a catastrophic intervention by God in the operation of the normal processes of nature. Therefore any application of the principle of uniformity, based on measurements of present processes, could not possibly extend back earlier than the time of the flood at best. Consequently, earth history earlier than this cannot be discerned geologically with any assurance; revelation is required.

The prophecy also indicates the modern fruit of this unjustifiable use of the uniformity principle and its resulting theory of evolution, namely, the widespread denial of the supernatural in general, and in particular the coming judgment at the imminent return of the Lord Jesus Christ.

In concluding our discussion of creation and the flood, it is well to note that, despite much propaganda to the contrary, there does exist a substantial minority of scientists who are creationists, men who believe in a recent special creation of all things and a universal flood, as taught in the Bible. For example, the Creation Research Society, organized in 1963, has at present (1968) a membership of over 350 qualified scientists, all with at least M.S. degrees and representing every field of science. All members of the society adhere to the above beliefs, as well as accepting the infallibility of Scripture and the deity of Christ. The society publishes a quarterly journal of research papers on different topics in biblical creationism and catastrophism (see Bibliography) as well as other literature. The Evolution Protest Movement is a somewhat similar organization in England. It is undoubtedly true that most scientists, as well as most representatives of other vocations, reject the authority of God's Word, but this is not because of their science!

4

THE BIBLE AND HISTORY

PROBABLY NO PARTS of the Bible have been more completely vindicated by modern discovery than those parts which deal with the history of the Jewish people and those nations with which they came in contact. It was once the custom of the higher critics to attack almost everything mentioned in the Bible as unhistorical, written long after the supposed events took place or, as like as not, simply fabricated by the writer. Since the multitude of archaeological discoveries made within the past century, however, the pendulum is swinging the other way and the Bible is regarded even by those who do not believe in its inspiration as an exceedingly trustworthy book from the historical standpoint.

It is well known that the earliest known civilizations of the world were those of Sumeria, Egypt, Babylonia, Assyria, and other countries in the region near the eastern shores of the Mediterranean. A tremendous amount of research has been applied to the study of the histories of these lands by modern archaeologists and historians. Their findings occupy literally hundreds of volumes, and we cannot begin to consider all of them here. However, it would be interesting to look at a few of the more striking examples of the Bible's vindication by archaeology and related fields.

Some of the most interesting of the Babylonian and Egyptian discoveries have to do with the period before the flood. In these and other countries have been discovered numerous stories of the creation, the fall, the antediluvian patriarchs, and the flood. Many of these stories bear striking similarities to the Bible accounts. Since many of them antedate the writing of Genesis by Moses, critics occasionally claim that he obtained his material from these sources and that consequently the Genesis record is merely legendary like the other stories. However, a mere comparison of the majestic account in the Bible with the garbled and mythological nonsense of practically all these other stories is sufficient evidence that the record of these events as given in the Bible is incomparably superior to all other records combined, a fact which can be accounted for only on the basis of inspiration. It is only natural to suppose that some recollection of such important happenings as the creation and the flood would be handed down by word of mouth to all the descendants of Adam and Noah. And it is extremely significant that in spite of their obviously legendary character, these spurious records show marked resemblance to the account given in the Bible. It seems certain that these stories must, therefore, have a definite factual basis.

The story of the dispersion of the peoples after building the Tower of Babel is usually cavilled at by Bible critics. Nevertheless, it is very likely that a part of the original tower is still standing. It has not been many years since what seemed to be the greatest of the Babylonian ziggurats was excavated. However, it was found from the Babylonian records that this tower was old during Babylon's heyday and had, in fact, been repaired and restored for use in her sacrificial worship. The Greek historian Herodotus, about 500 B.C., described the structure, which then consisted of a series of eight ascending towers, each one recessed in turn, with a spiral roadway running around it as a means of climbing to the top. At the very top was a great temple, which was used in the worship of Babylon's gods. Babylonian legend had it that this tower originally had been built by Nimrod, which coincides with the Bible record. In fact, the region is still called Birsnimroud by the Arabs. This great structure had a height of something over seven hundred feet, of which several hundred still remain. If this tower is not actually the original Tower of Babel, it probably at least was meant to be a replica of it, as indeed may have been true of many of the other ancient Mesopotamian ziggurats.

It has been difficult to find direct archaeological evidence bearing on the early patriarchs of Israel before the time of Joshua. This is, of course, explainable by the fact that Israel was not yet a nation; and it would be an extremely fortunate coincidence if relics of individuals such as Abraham, Isaac, Jacob, Joseph or Moses would be found. On the other hand there is quite a bit of collateral evidence which illumines the biblical stories and proves that the descriptions of the countries, peoples and general conditions of life during those times as given in the Bible are quite accurate and must have been written either by very trustworthy eyewitnesses or written under the inspiration of the Holy Spirit. For example, Abraham's boyhood home is mentioned in the Bible as Ur of the Chaldees. The location and the very existence of this place were at one time uncertain, but in recent years it has been discovered and fully explored. Critics at one time claimed that the Pentateuch could not have been written by Moses because the art of writing was unknown when he was living. Discoveries in Ur and other places, however, have proved beyond all doubt that writing was well developed for at least many hundreds of years before even Abraham's time. Furthermore, it is interesting here to note that the former "armchair theories" of the higher critics about the gradual evolution of culture, science, religion, etc., are gradually being demolished by each new archaeological discov-

ery. Recent explorations at great numbers of these ancient cities have revealed over and over again that the
earliest discoverable civilizations were the highest, and
that there was a constant degeneration in the arts and
sciences as time went on. It has even been shown that
their religion was originally monotheistic and later degraded into polytheism, rather than the other way
around, as formerly claimed.

The destruction of Sodom and Gomorrah by the
raining of fire and brimstone (sulphur) from the sky
sounds much like a volcanic eruption, a supposition
which is amply supported by an examination of the
region formerly occupied by these cities, on the shores
of the Dead Sea. The large quantities of sulphur and
bitumen, as well as the volcanic rocks and the sulphur-
ous gases generated in the soil all point back to some
tremendous holocaust of the past. Even the case of
Lot's wife becomes clearer in the light of these facts.
It is likely that she lagged behind (the probable meaning of "looked back") and was overcome in the catastrophe. There are huge beds of salt in the region, and
it may be that she was buried by a mass of salt thrown
in the air. The word translated "salt" does not necessarily denote sodium chloride, but might mean any
crystalline chemical compound. It is conceivable that
she was buried by the lava and later, through the
years and by the ordinary forces of nature, became
petrified or fossilized, thus actually turning into "salt."
This very thing is known to have happened to a great
many individuals in the volcanic destruction of the
Roman city of Pompeii. Furthermore, archaeological
explorations at the site prove definitely that the region
was inhabited during the time of Abraham, but immediately thereafter became barren of inhabitants and
remained so for about two thousand years.

The Hebrew captivity in Egypt, as well as the exodus are now, because of archaeological evidence, ac-

cepted as historical even by the critics, although
they were formerly concluded to be legendary.
The ten plagues, although no directly corroborative
evidence of them has yet been discovered, have attained added significance with the discovery that every
one of them seemed particularly aimed at some phase
of the religion of the Egyptians. The deities of the
Nile; the goddesses of the frog, the fly and the cattle;
the gods of medicine, the elements, the sun, the fer-
tility of the fields; and finally the goddess of birth,
all suffered tremendous loss of prestige in the minds
of the extremely polytheistic Egyptians because of the
plagues of Jehovah. Archaeology, by thus revealing the
religion of the Egypt of Moses' day, indirectly sub-
stantiates the Bible records and certainly endues them
with greater meaning.

Concerning the wanderings of the Israelites in the
wilderness, little of a secular nature is known other
than the fact that a people called Khabiri (possibly
the Hebrews) began overrunning the countries of
Canaan about this time. The conquest began with the
crossing of the Jordan and the destruction of Jericho,
both events being accomplished by means of miraculous help from God. The Bible relates that when the
priests bearing the ark of the covenant stepped to the
Jordan's edge, ". . . the waters which came down
from above stood and rose up upon an heap, very far
from the city . . . and the people passed over right
against Jericho." It is interesting that a similar thing
has happened at least three other times in history, the
last in 1927. Each time it has been caused by an up-
stream landslide, which left the riverbed below dry
for several hours. The Bible account could well describe a miraculously timed landslide and the resultant
damming of the waters.

The city of Jericho has been the focus of intensive
excavations for many years, especially by Garstang

and Kenyon. The former found evidence of the conquest of Jericho by Joshua in the manner described in the Bible. Later excavations by Kenyon, however, seemed to indicate that the occupation level described by Garstang was from a different time than that of Joshua. Evidently Jericho was rebuilt and reinhabited many times during its long history and there is still uncertainty as to the time, though not as to the fact, of Joshua's conquest.

Among the strongest of the peoples which the Hebrews had to face in the promised land were the Hittites. There are a great many references to these people in the Bible, but until the closing years of the nineteenth century, there was no external evidence that they ever existed. For many years the higher critics used the Hittite legend as one of their most telling blows against the inspiration of the Scriptures. Archaeological scholarship, however, has long since revealed that these people constituted one of the most powerful and influential nations of antiquity, thus once more demonstrating the weakness of the critical position and the truth of the Bible. The same story might be told of Edom and the Edomites, who are mentioned time and again in the Bible, but were completely forgotten in secular history until the nineteenth century, when references to them were found in Egyptian and Assyrian monuments. Finally, the splendidly preserved remains of their capital city, Petra, "the rock city," were discovered. Thus the critics, who had maintained the Edomites to be legendary, were again routed.

The very common critical view regarding the cruelty and injustice of Jehovah's instruction to the Israelites to exterminate the Canaanite inhabitants of the promised land must now be viewed in the light of archaeological discoveries relating to Canaanitish civilization and religion. These discoveries have demonstrated that Canaan had degenerated into an area of unbridled

wickedness and cruelty, including the extensive prac-
tice of child sacrifice, and accompanied by the grossest
immoralities regularly practiced in the guise of religion.
Their influence on God's people was bound to be
degenerating unless they were completely removed, and
in fact history demonstrated it to be so when Israel
failed to carry out God's command of extermination.

Many discoveries have also thrown light on the
periods of the judges and the kings of Israel, all
strongly supporting the historical accuracy of the Old
Testament accounts. King Solomon's great stables have
been unearthed, for example, as well as a great copper-
smelting furnace belonging to Solomon at his seaport
of Ezion-Geber. During the later period of the divided
kingdom, the Assyrian Empire was in its ascendancy
and power, and many discoveries in Assyrian archaeology also illumine and confirm the biblical histories.
The failure of Sennacherib to take Jerusalem from
King Hezekiah, in spite of the seeming invincibility of
his mighty army, is implied in one of the Assyrian's
cylinders, unearthed at the site of his ancient capital,
Nineveh. Hezekiah's pool and conduit, constructed during this time probably in anticipation of the coming
Assyrian siege, have been found still intact beneath
Jerusalem.

These are only a few of the great number of discoveries which have been made in the past century
confirmatory of the accuracy and authenticity of the
Old Testament histories. For a more detailed study
of this subject, the reader should read one of the
many recent conservative books on Biblical archaeology, such as those by Free, Unger, Pfeiffer, Allis,
and others.

Problems still exist, of course, in the complete harmonization of archaeological material with the Bible,
but none so serious as not to bear real promise of
imminent solution through further investigation.

It is significant that Dr. N. Nelson Glueck, probably the outstanding living Palestinian archaeologist, has said: "It may be stated categorically that no archaeological discovery has ever controverted a Biblical reference. Scores of archaeological findings have been made which confirm in clear outline or in exact detail historical statements in the Bible."[1]

We need to consider briefly the subject of the authenticity of the Old Testament writings. It has long been one of the chief tenets of modernism that most of the canonical books of the Old Testament were written long after the events they purport to describe and usually by other than the traditional authors, and that, as a consequence, they contain many anachronisms and errors. There is no proof of an objective nature of this claim, and yet this claim is almost always made in a very dogmatic way as one of the proved results of modern scholarship.

In particular, the Pentateuch and the book of Daniel have been maligned in this manner. By a critical examination of the words, phrases, etc., in the first five books of the Bible, critics have come to the conclusion that these books were written by several different writers, probably at a period just before or just after the Babylonian exile, instead of by Moses. This claim is made in spite of the fact that many of the New Testament writers and even Jesus Himself refer to these writings as being of Mosaic authorship. These men were much closer to the time of writing of the disputed books and were much better acquainted with their history than the modern critics. To deny the Mosaic authorship of the Pentateuch is to deny the deity of Christ. For if He was, as He claimed to be, the Son of God, surely He would not have spoken

---

[1]Nelson Glueck, *Rivers in the Desert* (New York: Grove, 1960), p. 31.

so frequently of Moses' writings as such, if Moses were not the author.

However, an unbiased examination of the books themselves surely must convince a reasonable person that they must have been written about the time of Moses. They abound with evidences of Egyptian influence. Even in the very early parts of Genesis, which are commonly supposed by the critics to have been derived from the Babylonian and Sumerian legends, there are many words, roots, and phrases that are very clearly borrowed from the Egyptian language.

Actually, it is probable that Moses was more properly the editor rather than the author of much of the book of Genesis. The phrase "these are the generations of" which occurs eleven times in Genesis, seems to mark off the original eyewitness narratives written by Adam, Noah and the other early patriarchs. These quite possibly were first written on stone tablets by the men whose names are thus recorded on the signature inscriptions and handed down through the patriarchal line, preserving the true history of the race from its very beginnings. They were finally acquired by Moses, who made the necessary editorial transitions and additions, and who then picked up the record himself in the writing of Exodus and the other books of the Pentateuch. Moses and the earlier patriarchs were certainly fully capable of writing, contrary to the claims of critics who ignore the testimony of modern archaeology on this subject. This explanation of Genesis accounts for the well-known style differences as well as all other linguistic and historical phenomena in Genesis.

As far as the other books of the Pentateuch are concerned, the critical theory is utterly unable to explain why such a large portion of the writings would have been taken up with details of the exodus and the wilderness wanderings. For example, why did

the supposed postexilic writers take so much time and
space to describe the minutest details of the construction of the tabernacle in the wilderness and the forms
of worship to be used in connection with it? Most
of the critics claim that the tabernacle never actually
existed. Finally, it is impossible to imagine the slightest
reason why these writers would have gone to such
great pains to deceive the people and clothe their
writings with a spurious antiquity, claiming them to
be the works of Moses. How was it possible that no
one, down through all the centuries, seemed to have
the slightest suspicion that these writings were not
genuine works of Moses until the modern higher critics
went to work on them? It is truly amazing that the
channel through which has come the highest code of
morals in the world and the purest and sublimest conception of God should have been contaminated with
intentional fraud at its source. If they were not really
what they were represented to be, it seems quite impossible that the books could have been received as
genuine at any time after that of Moses. They contain detailed instructions as to laws and civil and
ecclesiastical ordinances, which are presented as having
been in force from the time of Moses, and of the
institution and continued observance of the Passover,
which according to the records, had been observed
from the time of Moses. Such a book, or laws, or
priesthood, or ordinance could never have been accepted at a later date if they were not actually existing
at that time, and were believed by the people to have
been continually in force from the time of Moses.

Naturally, in a work of this nature, we cannot dwell
upon the details of the evidence for and against this
critical theory of the authorship of the Pentateuch and,
for that matter, other sections of the Old Testament
as well. However, for the student who is interested in
the subject, a wealth of literature is available. Every

claim and dogmatism of the critics has been adequately
answered and refuted by Christian scholars.

Let us briefly consider the book of Daniel, however.
Probably not even the books of Moses have been subjected to as much criticism and as many charges of
spurious antiquity as has this book. However, this was
to be expected because of the amazing prophecies in
the book, most of which have already been fulfilled
with meticulous accuracy. Consequently, it is claimed
that the book of Daniel was written after the events
predicted had already occurred, a position forced on
the critics for the simple reason that, if the genuineness of Daniel were admitted, the fulfillment of its
prophecies would constitute an incontrovertible proof
of its supernatural inspiration and by inference would
establish the fact that all of the Bible had been
given by inspiration of God. Some of these prophecies
and their fulfillments will be discussed in the next
chapter, but here we are concerned with the matter of
the historical authenticity of Daniel.

The book purports to have been written over a
rather long period of years, but all during the exile in
Babylon. It is written partially in Aramaic and partially in Hebrew, with portions which especially concerned the captive Jews being in the latter language
and those addressed especially to the Babylonians and
their King Nebuchadnezzar in the former. However,
the book contains three Greek words and this fact was
used as the basis of the assertion of the higher critics
that the book could not have been written until after
the conquest of Babylon by Alexander the Great.
Archaeology, however, has proved beyond any doubt
that there was extensive commerce between Greece and
Babylon even before the time of Nebuchadnezzar and
it is known that at least one of the questioned words
(all three of which were the names of Greek musical
instruments) was the name of an instrument which

had been in more or less common use in Babylon for many years before the time of Daniel. Not only did this "proof" backfire, but the existence in Daniel of eight Sumerian words would seem definitely to establish the time of writing as not later than Nebuchadnezzar's reign, for this language was never used after that and was almost a dead language at that time. Even the Hebrew language was no longer used after the captivity; so the fact that much of the book is written in Hebrew would imply that it was written before or during the captivity.

Considerable archaeological evidence has been brought to light that indirectly reveals the genuineness of the setting of the book of Daniel in the Babylon of Nebuchadnezzar and Cyrus. Excavations on the site of ancient Babylon have unearthed a building, the inscriptions on which show that it was used for the instruction of captive princes and nobles in the learning of the Chaldeans, thus indicating that the treatment of Daniel and his three friends by the Babylonians in such a gracious fashion at first was not at all foreign to the policies of that time, as formerly claimed by the critics. A huge furnace was discovered, with inscriptions to the effect that it was used to burn those who refused to worship the gods of the Babylonians, which shows that the story of the three Hebrews in the fiery furnace had a basis, at least, of fact. A large pit was discovered which was used for feeding to the wild beasts those men who disobeyed the decrees of the king. There was even a list of the ones who had been slain there, and Daniel's name was not among them. An inscription was discovered made by Nebuchadnezzar himself containing a strange story which many archaeologists are convinced corresponds to the period of the king's madness described by Daniel.

The most serious criticism of Daniel has lain in its supposed historical inaccuracies. According to Daniel, Belshazzar was king of Babylon at the time of the conquest of the Persians by Cyrus and was slain on the night of his drunken feast when the Persian army under Darius the Mede captured Babylon. But secular history said that Nabonidus was king of Babylon at the time and, furthermore, that he was not slain but carried away captive by the Persians. Of course, the critics made the most of this very obvious error, maintaining that Belshazzar was merely a nonexistent person invented by some later writer who was unfamiliar with history. But, through the years a great abundance of archaeological evidence has been accumulated which establishes beyond all doubt that Belshazzar actually did exist, although all historians but Daniel seemed to have forgotten all about him. Belshazzar, it is now known, was the son of Nabonidus and was a sort of regent over Babylon, serving in the place of his father, who was away from the city at the time of the Persian conquest. In other words, both Nabonidus and Belshazzar were kings of Babylon, in a very real sense, at that time. Archaeology has also revealed that Belshazzar actually was killed in his palace by the Persians on that fateful night.

The book of Isaiah also contains many marvelous prophecies, which were later fulfilled. Therefore, it has been commonly divided by the critics into at least two divisions, assigned to different authors at different periods of history, in spite of an abundance of external testimony and evidence against this notion. Jesus quoted from both of the two main divisions of Isaiah, and attributed both to the one Prophet Isaiah.

The discovery in 1948 of a very early copy of the book of Isaiah has been given wide publicity in the popular press. This manuscript has been dated at no later than 100 B.C., which is earlier by many centuries than any other extant Old Testament manuscripts. In view of this, it is very significant that the manuscript

is in all important particulars identical with the received Isaiah text, bearing a striking testimony to the
care and accuracy with which the Hebrew scribes
copied and transmitted the Scriptures. Most of the
few differences that do exist are merely matters of
spelling, and there are no discrepancies of any real
significance at all. There is no indication whatever
that the scribe regarded the book as being subdivisible
into two main parts, composed by different authors.

Since this first discovery, many other manuscripts
have been found in caves around the Dead Sea, probably deposited there by a pre-Christian sect known
as the Essenes. These manuscripts contain a large part
of the Old Testament, and are all essentially identical
with the Received Text, in spite of the fact that the
oldest copies previously available are dated some 900
to 1,000 years later than these Dead Sea Scrolls.

We could occupy several chapters with other details
of how the Old Testament has been and is being vindicated in a most wonderful way by the finds of archaeology. But let us consider briefly some of the discoveries of modern research in archaeology and textual
criticism which bear on the historicity and trustworthi-
ness of the New Testament.

Although it was formerly suggested by some critics
that Jesus was entirely a legendary character, in recent
years such a mass of evidence to the contrary has
been compiled that no informed person longer doubts
that Jesus actually lived and was at least a very great
religious leader and teacher. Numerous inscriptions
and papyri have been discovered that either mention
the name of Christ as the leader and founder of the
sect of the Christians, or that simply refer to the
Christians and their amazingly rapid growth. Many
of these date from the first or very early second centuries, and it is impossible to suppose that they all

resulted from the devotion of a group of fanatics to a legendary character.

It has also been well established now that the books of the New Testament are all completely authentic from the standpoint of authorship and antiquity. It was formerly charged that many of the books, if not all, were written long after the time of Jesus by men other than the traditional authors. This indictment was aimed not so much at the Pauline writings, however, as at the Gospels, especially that of John, and at the Acts. Especially in the latter book, it was long supposed that there were numerous gross historical inaccuracies and that, in fact, the whole tenor of the book belonged to a much later time than the days of the apostles. However, archaeology has completely refuted this claim. Practically all the towns and cities mentioned in Acts or in the Gospels have been located, with the finds at all these places being of such nature as to wholly vindicate the historical accuracy of the writers. There are many remains of the architecture of Herod throughout Palestine, although his temple in Jerusalem was completely destroyed by the Romans in 70 A.D. Well-preserved relics of a synagogue have been explored on the site of Capernaum. It is possible that this was the very synagogue in which Jesus occasionally preached. Of course, there are a great many sites and structures that are connected by tradition with Jesus and the apostles, but in most cases these are not susceptible of either proof or disproof.

Miniature images of Diana, such as described by Luke in the Acts, have been unearthed in Grecian cities. An altar was found dedicated to "the unknown God," probably similar to the one that Paul made the subject of his Athens sermon. The remains of the Areopagus, or Mars' hill, from which Paul delivered this sermon may still be seen.

Inscriptions have been found in great abundance,

some of which seem to contain names of people actually mentioned in the New Testament. Many Roman coins have been found, including the Roman penny with Caesar's likeness which Jesus observed and which prompted Him to caution His questioners to "render . . . unto Caesar the things which are Caesar's; and unto God the things that are God's" (Matt. 22:21). Inscriptions have been found describing the Roman census, which was taken, it seems, about every thirteen years. During one of these, Luke states, Jesus was born. Criticism long maintained that this was a definite historical error because there was no record of any Roman census at such an early date. Later discoveries have revealed otherwise, however, and it is now known that the census had been an established custom for many years previous.

All of these finds, as well as many others, date from apostolic times, and give the historical portions of the New Testament a definite vindication. Even when attacked from the linguistic side, the New Testament has emerged victorious. The oldest New Testament manuscripts extant were written in Greek, but in a form of Greek unknown to classical literature. A great many words were ascribed by the critics to later origin. However, it is known now, from many finds of papyri inscriptions dating from the first century and earlier, that this peculiar language, now known as Koine Greek, was the universal language of the common people of the Mediterranean world during the time of Christ and the apostles.

The book of John has been subjected to great criticism through the centuries, probably because of its superb presentation of Jesus as the Son of God, through whom alone men can be saved. Modern critics have dated its composition at some three or four centuries after Christ, because, they decided, its supposedly peculiar theology belonged to that period rather than to the first century. However, many evidences exist, from early second century writers who refer to or quote from John's gospel, that it was composed no later than 95 A.D. and by John himself.

In 1935 a part of John's gospel was found on a papyrus fragment which has been dated by all authorities as at least before 150 A.D. This has demonstrated conclusively that this gospel could not have been written later than about 100 A.D., which has always been maintained by the church. Similar papyrus evidence has come to light demonstrating the first century origin of the other Gospels.

There remains, however, the question of whether the events described in the books, especially those involving miracles, ever really took place or were invented by the writers as aids to the spread of the new religion. Then there is the question as to whether the character and life of Jesus were really as perfect as represented.

It will surely be admitted that all the facts of the New Testament record—the virgin birth, the miracles, the transfiguration, the sinless life—stand or fall with the truth or falsity of Jesus' resurrection from the dead. If Jesus died and rose again, which is the central and foundational belief of all true Christianity, then He must in truth have been very God, and there remains no rational difficulty in believing the other things, which upon analysis in the light of His resurrection become, in fact, quite necessary.

Did Jesus of Nazareth rise from the dead? To deny it means to deny on a priori grounds the specific testimony of six of the eight New Testament writers. The other two definitely imply their belief in and knowledge of the resurrection. As we have seen, these witnesses are all established as to date and authenticity. The descriptions of the resurrection morning and the later appearances of Christ in the four Gospels and in

Acts do not have the character of manufactured evidence. The differences in the accounts (which, however, are not contradictory but complementary) alone prove this. The different accounts would almost necessarily have been the same if the writers had connived on the tale. The Apostle Paul, acknowledged even by his critics to have been a man of great intellect and discernment, states that he was instantaneously changed from a Pharisee of the Pharisees to a Christian at the sight of the resurrected Christ. His great life and works prove the genuineness of his conversion. He states, in his first letter to the Corinthians, that more than five hundred people, many of whom were still living when he wrote, saw the risen Lord on one occasion.

There can be little doubt that Jesus actually was crucified and was dead when He was placed in the tomb. A Roman soldier thrust a sword into His side to assure himself that He really was dead, and saw blood mixed with water flow out, evidence of a hemorrhage in the heart cavity. He was placed in a tomb, covered from head to foot with graveclothes, and a Roman guard was set to watch the sealed tomb. It is unthinkable that He could merely have been in a sort of coma and could have recovered sufficiently to have removed the graveclothes and walked out of the tomb. Yet, it is also a fact of history that the tomb was empty early on the first day of the week following His crucifixion. The Pharisees and the Sadducees would certainly have produced the body if they could have done so in order to halt the rapidly growing Christian faith. And this rapid growth (there were over 5,000 converts in one day at Jerusalem on the Day of Pentecost) can only be explained by the fact that these people believed that the tomb of Christ was empty and also, for that matter, that many had seen Him since His resurrection.

But it might be argued that the disciples had actually stolen the body of Jesus from the tomb, as the Pharisees bribed the soldiers to testify. Of course, even if the soldiers of the watch *were* sleeping on guard, that very fact would have made it impossible for them to see the disciples steal the body; so no real proof could be offered. Besides, there is an overpowering moral and spiritual question involved. It is unthinkable that the greatest spiritual force and power of righteousness that the world has ever seen could have been founded on an intentional deception. The very change in character of the disciples themselves reveals the lie in this blasphemous charge. Men who had been weak, vacillating and doubting, suddenly became bold, powerful, Spirit-filled proclaimers of the gospel of salvation through faith in the risen Christ. They had nothing to gain materially from any such deception. Instead they were persecuted and regarded as mad fanatics, and most of them were finally put to death in the great Herodian and Roman persecutions. The uniform testimony of even the enemies of Christianity down through the centuries has been that the apostles and the thousands of other Christians that have been slain for their faith in Christ all died gloriously and unafraid. Men do not die like this for something they know to be a lie.

The very existence in the world of the Christian institutions of the church, the observance of Sunday, and the observance of Easter, all testify to the literal truth of the physical resurrection of Christ from the dead. All of these institutions can be traced back to about A.D. 30-40. Something extraordinary must have happened at that time to give them a start. Sabbath observance, for example, was one of the most rigidly adhered to of the Jewish laws and customs. Most of the early Christians had been very devout Jews. How is it possible, apart from the resurrection, to explain

the sudden change from Saturday to Sunday for the
religious services of these people?

The impact of Jesus Christ upon the world's history in the past 1,900 years is itself a unique testimony
to His own deity. Some people have considered this
influence harmful, citing as evidence certain evil practices or doctrines promulgated or condoned by certain
organized segments of so-called Christianity, especially
during the Middle Ages and Renaissance period.

But in spite of these things, which in most cases
have been shown to be chargeable to men or groups
who are not truly Christian in the biblical sense (true
Christians, of course, according to Scripture are those
who have received the Lord Jesus by faith as their
Saviour from sin), the great majority of men who
have honestly thought on the matter have recognized
that the impress of Christ and His followers upon the
world has been ennobling and uplifting to a degree
far surpassing that of all other teachers and philoso-
phers.

The souls and lives of numberless men and women
have been redeemed from sin, fear, despair and misery,
to peace, holiness and love. The morality of whole continents has been purified and elevated by the Christian
gospel. Schools, hospitals and benevolent institutions of
all kinds for the alleviation of suffering and advance of
true knowledge have been by-products of Christianity
by cumulated thousands. Jesus Christ has been the
inspiration and theme for the world's greatest music,
art and literature.

That all this and much more should result from the
life and teaching of an obscure Jewish carpenter (such
as Jesus of Nazareth was, if He were human only)
would be more miraculous and inconceivable than that
He should be, as He claimed, God's only and eternal
Son, become man for the purpose of redeeming man.
Humanly, He was born in a stable in a small village,

then was brought up in another village that was despised even by His Jewish countrymen, who themselves were then and have ever since been despised and often hated by the other peoples of the world. He had little formal education, no obvious cultural talents, no financial position and no political stature. He taught a small, motley, unpromising group of followers His doctrines, and made seemingly strange and impossible assertions and promises. Then, after only three and a half years of such teaching, He was unjustly crucified and died as a common criminal on a Roman cross.

Yet it was this Man who made statements which, if He were only a man, must immediately have stamped Him a preposterous liar or a mad fanatic. For example, He said on one occasion: "I am the light of the world: he that followeth me shall not walk in darkness, but shall have the light of life" (John 8:12).

If any mere man should ever say such a thing, it would immediately be interpreted by most sensible people as colossal conceit or even rank madness, especially if his human circumstances were those of Jesus. Yet the amazing thing is that for 2,000 years this statement coming from Him has sounded natural and true and trustworthy, and in fact has been demonstrated to be a marvelously fulfilled prophecy. For 2,000 years He *has* been the light of the world, inspiring all those institutions, individuals, and motives which have most contributed to all that is worthwhile in our present world. Those who have followed Him have *not* walked in darkness, but *have* had the light of life, and there are millions upon millions who have testified so. Many have willingly and gladly followed Him into places of hardness, even death, with no motive except love for Him, who died that they might have everlasting life.

It was also He who said: "Upon this rock [that is, upon that belief in Himself as the Son of God, as just confessed by Peter] I will build my church; and the gates of hell shall not prevail against it" (Matt. 16:18). This is also quite a ridiculous statement if made by one who was only a man, but the centuries have revealed its prophetic realism. Against the church of Jesus Christ (not an ecclesiastical organization, but the invisible body of those individuals who have shared Peter's confession of faith and have taken Christ into their hearts as Saviour and Lord) have been hurled all the weapons of destruction that hell could conceive —the force of empires, relentless and bloody persecution, intellectual rationalism which is even more deadly —and worst of all, the great burden of sin and indifference in the church itself. And yet they have not prevailed against it, even as He promised!

And again, He said: "Heaven and earth shall pass away, but my words shall not pass away" (Matt. 24:35). What a preposterous, presumptuous, outrageous claim for any man to make! But now in the twentieth century more than a few are fearing the earth's imminent destruction in atomic warfare. Biblical signs of the nearing end of the age are numerous. Yet Jesus' words are more widely distributed and believed by more people than ever before. More books, by far, have been written about Him and His words than those of any other man.

Through the centuries men have acclaimed Him as the world's greatest Teacher and its most perfect Man. In the light of all this, what reasonable conclusion is possible but that He is all that He claimed, and can and will fulfill all His marvelous promises to those who believe on Him?

The very center of His mission, His teaching and His gospel was the redemption of man from sin through His own sacrificial, atoning death for man's sin. The completion of all this is signalized and guaranteed by

His bodily resurrection from the dead, which has been declared again and again, by men trained and competent in the analysis of evidence, to be the best-demonstrated fact of all ancient history.

Thus, the Christian worships not a dead prophet or teacher or leader, but the living Son of God, whose bodily presence at the right hand of the Father in heaven is affirmed in Scripture, and whose spiritual presence in the Christian's own heart offers further and final daily attestation to the great fact of Christ's resurrection from the dead.

Finally, the history of the preservation and circulation of the Bible is itself a thrilling testimonial to the providential care of God for His Word. None of the original manuscripts have been preserved (if they had been, men would likely have elevated them to the status of sacred relics, or even idols), but so many thousands of copies were made and distributed in the early Christian centuries that any attempted suppression or corruption of the Scriptures quickly became impossible. Neither the fires of persecution nor the attacks of rationalistic unbelief has prevented the continued transmission of the Bible. Today, part or all of the Scriptures have been translated and published in 1,200 languages, and more copies by far have been printed than of any other book ever written. Furthermore, we can be quite confident that our present English Bible, in any of the standard translations, is substantially unchanged from its original form. Though each individual manuscript may contain errors of copying here and there, the vast number of early manuscripts, coming down through various channels of transmission, makes it possible for textual scholars to cross-check every passage in the most thorough manner. All such scholars are agreed that today we do have the Greek and Hebrew texts of the original writings, except for a small number of problem passages which are still somewhat uncertain. Thus we can be perfectly confident that when we read our Bibles we are reading the very Word of God!

5

FULFILLED PROPHECIES AND INTERNAL EVIDENCES

THE GREATEST DEMONSTRABLE EVIDENCE for the inspiration of the Scriptures, apart from the final, unanswerable proof of personal experience, lies in the fact that hundreds of prophecies contained in its pages have been remarkably fulfilled. In attempting to refute the evidence from predictive prophecy, critics have gone to absurd lengths. They have sought to explain away the fulfillments as coincidence, or have arbitrarily set the dates of the writing of the prophecies as subsequent to their fulfillment, or in most cases have simply ignored them. These attempts, however, have always been based on a process of rationalization rather than on demonstrable fact and, for the most part, have met utter defeat.

Bible prophecies are not vague and rambling, as is almost always true of certain supposed extrabiblical prophecies, such as those of Mother Shipton, Nostradamus, and others. Rather they deal with specific places, people and events, and their specific fulfillment can easily be checked by reference to subsequent history.

For example, consider the prophecy against that great city of antiquity, Tyre of the Phoenicians. It is found in Ezekiel 26, and first describes the coming capture of the city by Nebuchadnezzar (vv. 7-11). This was later fulfilled quite literally. However, the judgment forecast in verses 4-5: "They shall destroy the walls of Tyrus, and break down her towers: I will also scrape her dust from her, and make her like the top of a rock. It shall be a place for the spreading of nets in the midst of the sea," seemed unfulfilled. History tells us that most of the people of Tyre escaped with their valuables to an island half a mile from the shore, where they built a new Tyre which was still great and powerful for almost 250 years. But finally Alexander the Great finished what Nebuchadnezzar had begun. In his campaign of conquest through the East, the people of Tyre refused to surrender to him, and he seemingly had no way to reach the island city to capture it. However, he devised the ingenious plan of building a causeway from the mainland. The Macedonians then literally scraped the dust of the old mainland city and laid her stones and timber and dust in the midst of the water (see v. 12) to build the causeway. (Note the change from the "he," Nebuchadnezzar, in v. 11 to "they" in v. 12, indicating different conquerors.) The causeway was thus built from the remains of the old city and the island city was captured and sacked. Verse 21 says: "I will make thee a terror, and thou shalt be no more: though thou be sought for, yet shalt thou never be found again, saith the Lord GOD." The mainland city of Tyre, against which the prophecy was directed, was never rebuilt. There are not even ruins or mounds to mark the spot, which can only be approximately located from the writing of ancient historians. The causeway and island now form a desolate peninsula, which is used only by fishermen, for the purpose of "spreading their nets" for drying.

Tyre's sister city of Sidon had the following prophecy uttered against her: "Behold, I am against thee, O Sidon . . . . For I will send pestilence into her, and blood into her streets; and the wounded shall fall in the midst of her with the sword upon her on every side" (Ezek. 28:22-23, ASV). No fate of extinction was foretold for Sidon and even today it is a city of

about 20,000. However, it has had one of the blood-
iest histories any city ever had. It was almost destroyed
by the Persians, was the scene of many fierce battles
during the Crusades, and during the wars between the
Druses and the Turks, and later between the Turks
and the French. In 1840, Sidon was again the scene
of bloodshed when it was bombarded by the fleets of
three nations.

Two sister cities, close together and equal in importance, were thus the subjects of two very different
prophecies. Each has been fulfilled to the letter. That
would have been impossible except as directed by God,
who alone "knows the end from the beginning."

Many other cities have been singled out by the
prophets. We could not begin to discuss here the detailed fulfillment of all these predictions. However,
some of the cities and the corresponding prophecies
are listed below for the reader's reference:

> Thebes, Egypt (the "No" of Scripture)—Ezekiel
> 30:14-16
>
> Memphis, Egypt (the "Noph" of Scripture)—
> Ezekiel 30:13
>
> Ashkelon, Philistia—Zechariah 9:5
>
> Ekron, Philistia, also Gaza, Philistia—Zephaniah
> 2:4
>
> Bethel—Amos 3:14-15
>
> Samaria—Micah 1:6-7
>
> Jericho—Joshua 6:26
>
> Capernaum, Bethsaida and Chorazin—Matthew
> 11:20-23
>
> Babylon—Isaiah 13:19-22

All these and many other prophecies directed against
specific cities either have been or are being fulfilled
with meticulous accuracy.

Many countries also have been the subject of prophecy. Edom, or Idumea, was a nation that was located
next to the Jews in Palestine. Although the Edomites

were descended from Esau and were thus related to
the Israelites, they were extremely idolatrous and
treacherous and were constantly warring with the
Hebrew nation. Their land was very rugged and their
capital city, Petra, had a seemingly impregnable position in the rocks of the mountains. It was a very great
and rich city, being the terminus of one of the great
trade routes of the East; and even today its ruined
buildings and palaces, carved out of the solid rock,
are most imposing and magnificent. But in Ezekiel
35:3-9; Jeremiah 49:16-18, and other places, there
were predictions of the ultimate overthrow of Edom.
Edom was to be an utter desolation; her trade was to
cease, and all her inhabitants were to disappear. For
many centuries after they were written these prophecies
remained in the Scriptures without being fulfilled. Even
for some six hundred years after Christ, Edom and
Petra remained great and prosperous. But somehow,
sometime, a change came. Seemingly no one knows the
story. Now the whole land of Edom, as far as the city
of Maan, is utterly desolate, with practically no human
inhabitants, and very little animal life. It is interesting
that only Maan, a town on the east of Edom and the
Teman of Scripture, has escaped the desolation. But
this is precisely what was predicted in Ezekiel 25:13:
"I will make it desolate from Teman."

A similar judgment of perpetual extinction was predicted for the Philistines, another great and warlike
people of antiquity. They lived west of the Israelites,
on the seacoast, and were almost constantly fighting
with them. It was from the Philistines that much of the
Jewish trouble with idolatry was derived. Consequently,
we have the prophecy in Zephaniah 2:5-6 (ASV):
"The word of Jehovah is against you, O Canaan, the
land of the Philistines; I will destroy thee, that there
shall be no inhabitant. And the sea-coast shall be
pastures, with cottages for shepherds and folds for

flocks." There are several other similar prophecies against the Philistines, including some directed against specific Philistine cities, as noted before. Eventually, however, the Philistines all vanished and their country was taken over by others. Until its modern inclusion in the state of Israel, the ancient land of the Philistines was thereafter used almost exclusively for grazing and agriculture.

The nation of Egypt, on the other hand, was not doomed to extinction, as were Babylonia, Edom, Philistia and others. Egypt was one of the greatest powers of the ancient world, but in passage after passage of Scripture she was threatened with a gradual and permanent decline, but not with extinction. Ezekiel 29:15 says: "It shall be the basest of kingdoms; neither shall it exalt itself any more above the nations: for I will diminish them, that they shall no more rule over the nations." Today that prophecy still stands unchallenged. The so-called kingdom still exists; the people of Egypt today are the direct descendants of those who were at one time the greatest people in the world. Yet it is truly the basest of kingdoms and has no more exalted itself above the nations. There are a great many other predictions regarding Egypt, concerning such miscellaneous details as its industries, the weavers, the fisheries, the papyrus plants, the rivers and canals, its rulers, its exploitation by outsiders, the desolation of the country, etc. Every one of these has been fulfilled in a most marvelous way.

We have not the space to discuss more of these predictions here but should mention that such countries as Moab, Ammon, Chaldea, Assyria, Ethiopia and others are the subjects of biblical prophecies, all of which have been fulfilled.

We should consider briefly the Jewish people, however. Their entire history has been foretold in the Bible in a great number of prophecies, most of which have already been fulfilled. In Deuteronomy 28, even before the Israelites had entered the promised land, Moses predicted their future happiness in the land, their sufferings and punishments for disobedience, and finally their great worldwide dispersion. In chapter 30, he promised their eventual return, a prophecy which seemed impossible fifty years ago, but which is now being marvelously fulfilled. Their dispersion was prophesied by many others, including Christ Himself, as well as the terrible persecution that would be theirs in all nations. But it was also revealed that they would not be destroyed or assimilated but their national identity would be retained. Today the nation of Israel has been reestablished in its ancient land, and even the city of Jerusalem again belongs to the Jews.

The book of Daniel contains what are usually regarded as the most marvelous prophecies in the Bible. In chapters 2, 7, 8 and 11 of this book, the entire history of the world is foretold from the time of Nebuchadnezzar to the end. The careers of Babylonia, Medo-Persia, Greece, Egypt, Syria and Rome are described with such wealth of description and detail that no one acquainted with the facts of history can be uncertain as to the events and nations referred to. This very minuteness of detail is the sole remaining crutch of the critical school which has long contended that the book of Daniel was written after those events had transpired. The rationalism of the critics rules out the miracle of predictive prophecy, so this contention is absolutely necessary for them. Although it must be admitted that they still cling to it as a matter of necessity, it has been almost irrefutably proved, as shown in the preceding chapter, that the book is authentic both as to date and author, and thus its marvelous prophecies stand completely vindicated.

One of the most remarkable of all prophecies is found in Daniel 9:24-26, known as the prophecy of the seventy weeks. This prophecy was given to Daniel through the angel Gabriel, revealing the future history of his people Israel, including the exact time of the coming of the promised Messiah (Christ). It was given about 540 B.C., while Israel was in captivity in Babylon, with the city of Jerusalem and the great temple of God in ruins. Daniel was told that prophetic time would begin again for Israel when a command was given to rebuild Jerusalem. This command was given by Artaxerxes to Nehemiah in 445 B.C. (Neh. 2:5-8).

From this date, the prophecy indicated that 483 years (i.e., 69 "weeks," literally "sevens," meaning seven-year periods) would elapse until the coming of Messiah as Prince of Israel. Allowing for errors in our present system of chronology (Jesus was actually born about 5 B.C.) and for possible use of a prophetic year of 360 days instead of an actual solar year, it is obvious that this period culminated at about the time of the public ministry of Christ. In fact, Sir Robert Anderson and others have shown that, with certain reasonable assumptions, its fulfillment occurred on *the very day* that Christ for the first time accepted and encouraged His recognition as King of Israel, the day of His so-called "triumphal entry" into Jerusalem, a week before His rejection and crucifixion. Later, weeping over His rejection by His people, He said: "If thou hadst known, even thou, at least in *this thy day,* the things which belong unto thy peace, but now they are hid from thine eyes!" (Luke 9:42).

The prophecy also foretold that after His coming He would be "cut off" and would "have nothing." That is, He would be rejected as King by Israel, and this was of course exactly what happened. Certain other portions of this great prophecy have apparently not yet been fulfilled but are awaiting Christ's return and the full establishment of His kingdom for their final development and realization.

There are many other prophecies relating to the coming of Christ, possibly not as striking as this but just as miraculous. His virgin birth was predicted in Isaiah 7:14. His birthplace in Bethlehem was given in Micah 5:2. Zechariah 9:9-10 describes His public entry into Jerusalem on the foal of an ass. Many details of His teaching and healing ministries are given in various prophecies. His betrayal is described, including even the price of thirty pieces of silver, in Zechariah 11:12-13. The details of the crucifixion are most graphically portrayed in Psalm 22, written by David at a time when offenders were killed by stoning and crucifixion was unheard of, being a distinctively Roman method of punishment. The purpose of His death, as well as several of the details of His trial, suffering on the cross, and His burial are foretold in Isaiah 53. The fact that He died, not for Himself or anything that He had done, but as a substitute for our sins, is most vividly described here. Even the resurrection is indicated in several places in the Old Testament, as well as being foretold several times by Jesus Himself.

There are more than three hundred prophecies in the Old Testament which were fulfilled by Christ at His first coming. In an attempt to determine the scientific significance of these prophetic fulfillments, a California mathematician, Peter Stoner, made an interesting experiment with one of his classes. Each member of the class was assigned a particular Messianic prophecy for study, with the purpose of determining the statistical chance that the particular event could have been predicted without supernatural inspiration. For example, the prophecy in Micah 5:2 says that the Messiah would be born in Bethlehem. There was no more reason for this town to be chosen than any other town in Israel. Therefore its probability of chance fulfillment would be one divided by the number of towns in Israel at the time. In this manner, probabilities of fulfillment were determined for each of forty-eight Messianic prophecies.

Now the laws of mathematical probability show that the probability of several chance occurrences, independent of each other, being accomplished simultaneously is the product of the probabilities of all the individual occurrences. Thus the probability of all these forty-eight prophecies being fulfilled simultaneously in one individual, the promised Messiah and Saviour, was calculated as the product of all the separate probabilities. Professor Stoner found that the resultant probability was one chance out of a number that would be written as one, followed by 181 zeros.

To realize the significance of this tremendous number, visualize a huge ball composed of solidly packed electrons. These are the smallest entities we know anything about; it would take about two and one-half million billion of them to make a line one inch long. The largest thing we know anything about is our physical universe, some four billion light-years in radius (a light-year being the distance light travels in a year, moving at the speed of over 186,000 miles per second). However, our ball of electrons must have a diameter some five hundred quadrillion times as great as the diameter of our universe.

One of these electrons now is marked to distinguish it from all the rest, and then the entire mass stirred and mixed thoroughly. A blindfolded man is then sent into the ball to find the marked electron. *The chance that he would select the right electron on the first trial is roughly equivalent to the chance that these forty-eight prophecies could have been fulfilled without supernatural inspiration.*

All of which amounts to clear mathematical proof that the Scriptures must have been divinely inspired.

Most scientific laws have been established on the basis of statistical probabilities far less imposing than the above. And it must be remembered that these represented only forty-eight out of more than three hundred Messianic prophecies, and also that there are still hundreds of other fulfilled prophecies in the Bible. Surely a right-thinking person must conclude that truly the Bible is the very Word of God. Such phenomena as these are found in no other book in all the world!

There is another significant set of prophecies which are excitingly being fulfilled in these days before our very eyes. These prophecies describe conditions in the world shortly before the promised return of the Lord Jesus Christ to this earth "in flaming fire taking vengeance on them that know not God, and that obey not the gospel of our Lord Jesus Christ" (II Thess. 1:8).

Perhaps the most significant of these "signs of the times" is the restoration of Israel to her own ancient land as a recognized nation among nations. This amazing restoration, with a large number of its details, was promised in many passages of the Bible as an event that would occur in the last days of this age. (See e.g., Isa. 11:10-12; Jer. 23:3-8; 30:3-11; Ezek. 20:34-38; 36:24-35; 37:11-28). Of course, the complete fulfillment of such passages as these awaits a great coming divine judgment on Israel and her national conversion to Christ when He returns to earth to reign (Zech. 12:10—14:11).

The rise of Russia to world prominence and especially its emergence as a Mediterranean power at the head of a confederacy of nations encircling and attempting to destroy restored Israel is clearly indicated in Ezekiel 38. "Gog" in this chapter, the leader of this invasion attempt, is called the "prince of Rosh" (v. 2, ASV), and there are numerous other marks of identification clearly showing that Russia, in the latter days, is the nation referred to. The prophecy has not yet been fulfilled, but events are very rapidly developing in that direction.

Other important prophetic portents of the last days include the following:

Rapid increase of science, communication and travel (Dan. 12:4).

General moral and spiritual deterioration (II Tim. 3:1-7, 12-13).

Doctrinal apostasy of religious leaders (I Tim. 4:1-3; II Peter 2:1-2; II Tim. 4:3-4).

Antisupernaturalism among intellectual leaders (II Peter 3:3-6; II Tim. 3:5).

Conflicts between capitalistic and laboring classes (James 5:1-8).

Preparations for world government and world religion (Rev. 13:7-8).

Widespread materialism and secularism (Luke 17:26-30; 18:8).

Intermittent outbreaks of worldwide wars, famines and diseases (Luke 21:10-11).

The above prophecies and many others are being fulfilled in these present days, and the conditions they describe appear to become more serious with each passing day. Evidently, as both Scripture and current history plainly teach, world conditions will become increasingly perilous and anti-Christian as the return of the Lord draws near. However, there is one other prophecy of the latter times that is entirely different in character, namely, that the gospel will be preached as a witness to all nations before the end comes (Acts 1:8-11; Matt. 24:14; II Peter 3:9-15). Although there are some lands where the gospel has not yet really been preached, there has been a tremendous extension of evangelical Christian missions in recent generations. The Bible has been translated, at least in part, into more than 1,120 tongues to date. A number of mission boards are concentrating particularly on reaching hitherto unevangelized areas and tribes. Modern inventions such as the radio and airplane are contributing significantly to world evangelization, which seems well within the possibility of accomplishment in this generation. By doing all within our personal power to aid in the cause of world missions, it seems that we can actually speed the fulfillment of this prophecy, and thus hasten "the coming of the day of God" (II Peter 3:12).

Thus, as the world deteriorates and ripens for judgment, the gospel of Christ is nevertheless being taken to 'the ends of the earth. And all of these things both add to the tremendous evidences of the truth of Scripture and of the Christian faith, and also prove that the coming of the Lord Jesus must be very near!

For any reader who does not yet know the joy and assurance of personal salvation, may the author urge him with all his heart to receive the Lord Jesus by faith as Son of God and personal Saviour, committing his life and soul fully to Him. "For God so loved the world, that he gave his only begotten Son, that whosoever believeth in him should not perish, but have everlasting life" (John 3:16).

"Behold, *now* is the accepted time; behold, *now* is the day of salvation" (II Cor. 6:2).

Moody Press, a ministry of the Moody Bible Institute, is designed for education, evangelization, and edification. If we may assist you in knowing more about Christ and the Christian life, please write us without obligation: Moody Press, c/o MLM, Chicago, Illinois 60610.

Recommended References for Further Study

Note: The books suggested below have have selected with the following requirements in mind:

1. They are written from the perspective of full belief in complete biblical inspiration and, in most cases, represent also the viewpoint advanced by the author in the chapter for which they are listed.

2. They are sufficiently recent so as to be still in print or otherwise easily available for study. Some are recent reprints of older works.

3. They are scholarly works, well deserving of study, and yet are sufficiently nontechnical and lucid for the average reader to understand and enjoy.

Chapter 1

Aalders, G. C. *The Problem of the Book of Jonah.* London: Tyndale, 1949. Pp. 30.

Benson, Clarence H. *The Greatness and Grace of God.* Wheaton, Ill.: Scripture Press, 1953. Pp. 224.

Chesnut, D. Lee *The Atom Speaks.* Grand Rapids: Eerdmans, 1951. Pp. 232.

Clark, Robert E. D. *The Universe: Plan or Accident?* London: Paternoster, 1949. Pp. 192.

Coder, S. Maxwell and Howe, George F. *The Bible, Science and Creation.* Chicago: Moody, 1966. Pp. 128.

Hills, Edward F. *Space Age Science.* Des Moines: Christian Research, 1964. Pp. 84.

McMillen, S. I. *None of These Diseases.* Westwood, N. J.: Revell, 1963. Pp. 158.

Morris, Henry M. *Science, Scripture and Salvation.* Denver: Baptist Pubns., 1965. Pp. 160.

————. *Studies in the Bible and Science.* Philadelphia: Presbyterian & Reformed, 1966. Pp. 186.

Short, A. Rendle. *The Bible and Modern Medicine.* Chicago: Moody, 1953. Pp. 160.

————. *Wonderfully Made.* London: Paternoster, 1951. Pp. 159.

Whitcomb, John C. *Origin of the Solar System*. Philadelphia: Presbyterian & Reformed, 1964. Pp. 34.

Wood, Nathan R. *The Secret of the Universe*. Grand Rapids: Eerdmans, 1955. Pp. 220.

Chapter 2

Bales, James D. and Clark, Robert T. *Why Scientists Accept Evolution*. Philadelphia: Presbyterian & Reformed, 1966. Pp. 113.

Clark, Harold W. *Wonders of Creation*. Mountain View, Calif.: Pacific, 1964. Pp. 134.

Clark, Robert E. D. *Darwin: Before and After*. Chicago: Moody, 1967. Pp. 192.

Cousins, Frank W. *Fossil Man*. Hayling Island, Hants, England: Evolution Protest Movement, 1966. Pp. 106.

Custance, Arthur C. *Primitive Cultures—Their Historical Origins*. Ottawa: Doorway Papers. Pp. 84.

Dewar, Douglas. *The Transformist Illusion*. Murfreesboro, Tenn.: DeHoff, 1955. Pp. 306.

de Wit, J. J. Duyvene. *A New Critique of the Transformist Principle in Evolutionary Biology*. Kampen, Netherlands: J. H. Kok, 1964. Pp. 62.

Enoch, H. *Evolution or Creation*. Madras: Union of Evangelical Students of India, 1966. Pp. 172.

Frair, Wayne and Davis, P. William. *The Case for Creation*. Chicago: Moody, 1967. Pp. 96.

Hughes, Philip E. *Christianity and the Problem of Origins*. Philadelphia: Presbyterian & Reformed, 1964. Pp. 39.

Klotz, John W. *Genes, Genesis and Evolution*. St. Louis: Concordia, 1955. Pp. 575.

Marsh, Frank L. *Life, Man and Time*. Escondido, Calif.: Outdoor Pictures, 1967. Pp. 238.

Morris, Henry M. *Evolution and the Modern Christian*. Philadelphia: Presbyterian & Reformed, 1967. Pp. 72.

————. *The Twilight of Evolution*. Grand Rapids: Baker, 1964. Pp. 103.

Nelson, Byron C. *After Its Kind*. Minneapolis: Bethany Fellowship, 1967. Pp. 200.

Rushdoony, Rousas J. *The Mythology of Science*. Nutley, N.J.: Craig, 1967. Pp. 134.

Shute, Evan. *Flaws in the Theory of Evolution*. Philadelphia: Presbyterian & Reformed, 1962. Pp. 286.

Taylor, Hebden. *Evolution and the Reformation of Biology*. Nutley, N. J.: Craig, 1967. Pp. 62.

Tilney, A. G. (ed.). *The Case Against Evolution*. Hayling Island, Hants, England: Evolution Protest Movement, 1964.

Tinkle, William J. *Heredity: A Study in Science and the Bible*. Houston: St. Thomas, 1967. Pp. 180.

Young, Edward J. *Studies in Genesis One*. Philadelphia: Presbyterian & Reformed, 1964. Pp. 105.

Zimmerman, Paul A. (ed.). *Darwin, Evolution and Creation*. St. Louis: Concordia, 1959. Pp. 231.

Chapter 3

Clark, Harold W. *Fossils, Flood· and Fire*. Escondido, Calif.: Outdoor Pictures, 1968. Pp. 239.

———. *Genesis and Science*. Nashville: Southern, 1967. Pp. 128.

Cook, Melvin A. *Prehistory and Earth Models*. London: Max Parrish, 1966. Pp. 353.

Lammerts, Walter E. (ed.). *Quarterly Journal*, Creation Research Society, Ann Arbor.

Nelson, Byron C. *The Deluge Story in Stone*. Minneapolis: Bethany Fellowship, 1968. Pp. 190.

Price, George M. *Common-Sense Geology*. Mountain View, Calif.: Pacific, 1946. Pp. 239.

———. *The Story of the Fossils*. Mountain View, Calif.: Pacific, 1954. Pp. 73.

Rehwinkel, Alfred A. *The Flood*. St. Louis: Concordia, 1951. Pp. 372.

Whitcomb, John C. and Morris, Henry M. *The Genesis Flood*. Philadelphia: Presbyterian & Reformed, 1960. Pp. 518.

Whitney, Dudley J. *Face of the Deep*. New York: Vantage, 1955. Pp. 102.

———. *Genesis Versus Evolution*. New York: Exposition, 1961. Pp. 61.

Chapter 4

Adam, Ben. *The Origin of Heathendom.* Minneapolis: Bethany Fellowship, 1963. Pp. 128.

Allis, Oswald T. *The Five Books of Moses.* Philadelphia: Presbyterian & Reformed, 1947. Pp. 319.

Blaiklock, E. M. *Out of the Earth.* Grand Rapids: Eerdmans, 1961. Pp. 92.

Bruce, F. F. *Are the New Testament Documents Reliable?* Grand Rapids: Eerdmans, 1954. Pp. 122.

Custance, Arthur C. *A Study of the Names in Genesis 10.* Ottawa: Doorway Papers, 1964. Pp. 80.

————. *Remarkable Confirmations of Genesis from Archaeology.* Ottawa: Doorway Papers, 1963. Pp. 60.

Deissmann, Gustav A. *Light from the Ancient East.* Grand Rapids: Baker, 1965. Pp. 704.

Free, Joseph P. *Archaeology and Bible History.* Wheaton, Ill.: Scripture Press, 1950. Pp. 398.

Greenleaf, Simon. *The Testimony of the Evangelists.* Grand Rapids: Baker, 1965. Pp. 613.

Hanke, Howard A. *The Validity of the Virgin Birth.* Grand Rapids: Zondervan, 1963. Pp. 122.

Machen, J. Gresham. *The Virgin Birth of Christ.* New York: Harper, 1930. Pp. 415.

Morison, Frank. *Who Moved the Stone?* New York: Barnes & Noble, 1962. Pp. 192.

Otten, Herman. *Baal or God.* New Haven, Mo.: Leader, 1965. Pp. 353.

Pfeiffer, Charles F. *The Biblical World.* Grand Rapids: Baker, 1966. Pp. 612.

————. *The Dead Sea Scrolls.* Grand Rapids: Baker, 1962. Pp. 119.

Thomas, W.H.G. *Christianity Is Christ.* Grand Rapids: Eerdmans, 1955. Pp. 161.

Thompson, J. A. *The Bible and Archaeology.* Grand Rapids: Eerdmans, 1962. Pp. 468.

Unger, Merrill F. *Archaeology and the New Testament.* Grand Rapids: Zondervan, 1962. Pp. 337.

————. *Archaeology and the Old Testament.* Grand Rapids: Zondervan, 1954. Pp. 339.

Whitcomb, John C. *Darius the Mede.* Grand Rapids: Eerdmans, 1959. Pp. 79.

Wilson, Robert Dick. *A Scientific Investigation of the Old Testament*. Chicago: Moody, 1959. Pp. 194.

Wiseman, P. J. *New Discoveries in Babylonia about Genesis*. London: Marshall, Morgan & Scott, 1946. Pp. 143.

Yamauchi, Edwin M. *Greece and Babylon*. Grand Rapids: Baker, 1966. Pp. 115.

Zwemer, Samuel M. *The Origin of Religion*. New York: Loizeaux, 1945. Pp. 256.

Chapter 5

Anderson, Robert. *The Coming Prince*. Grand Rapids: Kregel, 1954. Pp. 311.

Cooke, A. Ernest. *Fulfilled Prophecy*. Chicago: Moody, 1963. Pp. 64.

Custance, Arthur C. *Striking Fulfillments of Prophecy*. Ottawa: Doorway Papers. Pp. 32.

Davis, George T. B. *Bible Prophecies Fulfilled Today*. Philadelphia: Million Testaments Campaign, 1955. Pp. 111.

Hull, William L. *The Fall and Rise of Israel*. Grand Rapids: Zondervan, 1954. Pp. 424.

Newell, Philip R. *Daniel—the Man Greatly Beloved and His Prophecies*. Chicago: Moody, 1962. Pp. 199.

Pentecost, J. Dwight. *Things to Come*. Findlay, Ohio: Dunham, 1958, Pp. 633.

Smith, Wilbur M. *Egypt in Biblical Prophecy*. Boston: W. A. Wilde, 1957. Pp. 256.

————. *Israeli-Arab Conflict and the Bible*. Glendale, Calif.: Gospel Light, 1967. Pp. 162.

————. *World Crises and the Prophetic Scriptures*. Chicago: Moody, 1951. Pp. 384.

Stewart, Herbert. *The Stronghold of Prophecy*. London: Marshall, Morgan & Scott, 1941. Pp. 127.

Stoner, Peter. *Science Speaks*. Chicago: Moody, 1952. Pp. 128.

Urquhart, John. *Wonders of Prophecy*. London: Pickering & Inglis, 1949. Pp. 241.

Walvoord, John F. *The Nations in Prophecy*. Grand Rapids: Zondervan, 1967. Pp. 176.